Contact

Documentation

Author's Note

Greetings Fellow Educators,

We are tasked to do so much more than teach. Aside from all the different hats we wear in the classroom, I feel like we also have to be our own secretary with all the calls and paperwork. There's not enough time in the day for us. So, in trying to help myself, I wanted to also help you. I am always happy with any product that will help me save some time. I hope this book helps save you some precious minutes in documenting your communication about students.

Thank you for supporting my effort with your purchase. Enjoy!

Yours in Education,

Cynthia Thompson

School Year

_____

Contact Documentation Form

Student Name: _____   Class: _____

Date and Time: _____   Person Initiating: _____

Person Contacted	☐ Parent/Guardian:
	☐ Counselor:
	☐ Nurse:
	☐ Administrator:
	☐ Other:

Type of Contact	☐ Phone Call/Text	☐ Email
	☐ Informal Meeting	☐ Letter/Note
	☐ Arranged Meeting	☐ Class Dojo
	☐ Other: _____	

Phone Call Response	☐ No Answer	☐ Wrong Number _____	☐ Left Voicemail	☐ Sent Text

Topic Discussed	☐ Grades	☐ Behavior
	☐ Homework	☐ Class work
	☐ Projects	☐ Schedule Meeting
Notes/Other:		

Action to be Taken:

Contact Purpose	☐ Glow	☐ Grow

Life has 2 rules. #1-Never Quit #2-Always remember rule #1 – Unknown

Contact Documentation Form

Student Name: _____ Class: _____

Date and Time: _____ Person Initiating: _____

Person Contacted	☐ Parent/Guardian:
	☐ Counselor:
	☐ Nurse:
	☐ Administrator:
	☐ Other:

Type of Contact	☐ Phone Call/Text	☐ Email
	☐ Informal Meeting	☐ Letter/Note
	☐ Arranged Meeting	☐ Class Dojo
	☐ Other: _____	

Phone Call Response	☐ No Answer	☐ Wrong Number _____	☐ Left Voicemail	☐ Sent Text

Topic Discussed	☐ Grades	☐ Behavior
	☐ Homework	☐ Class work
	☐ Projects	☐ Schedule Meeting
Notes/Other:		

Action to be Taken:

Contact Purpose	☐ Glow	☐ Grow

Out of a mountain of despair, a stone of hope. — Martin Luther King, Jr.

Contact Documentation Form

Student Name: _____   Class: _____

Date and Time: _____   Person Initiating: _____

Person Contacted	☐ Parent/Guardian:
	☐ Counselor:
	☐ Nurse:
	☐ Administrator:
	☐ Other:

Type of Contact	☐ Phone Call/Text	☐ Email
	☐ Informal Meeting	☐ Letter/Note
	☐ Arranged Meeting	☐ Class Dojo
	☐ Other: _____	

Phone Call Response	☐ No Answer	☐ Wrong Number _____	☐ Left Voicemail	☐ Sent Text

Topic Discussed	☐ Grades	☐ Behavior
	☐ Homework	☐ Class work
	☐ Projects	☐ Schedule Meeting

Notes/Other:

Action to be Taken:

Contact Purpose	☐ Glow	☐ Grow

Act as if what you do makes a difference. IT DOES. – *William James*

Contact Documentation Form

Student Name: _____   Class: _____

Date and Time: _____   Person Initiating: _____

Person Contacted	☐ Parent/Guardian:
	☐ Counselor:
	☐ Nurse:
	☐ Administrator:
	☐ Other:

Type of Contact	☐ Phone Call/Text	☐ Email
	☐ Informal Meeting	☐ Letter/Note
	☐ Arranged Meeting	☐ Class Dojo
	☐ Other: _____	

Phone Call Response	☐ No Answer	☐ Wrong Number _____	☐ Left Voicemail	☐ Sent Text

Topic Discussed	☐ Grades	☐ Behavior
	☐ Homework	☐ Class work
	☐ Projects	☐ Schedule Meeting

Notes/Other:

Action to be Taken:

Contact Purpose	☐ Glow	☐ Grow

Nothing is impossible. The word itself says "I'm possible!" – *Audrey Hepburn*

Contact Documentation Form

Student Name: _____   Class: _____

Date and Time: _____   Person Initiating: _____

Person Contacted	☐ Parent/Guardian:
	☐ Counselor:
	☐ Nurse:
	☐ Administrator:
	☐ Other:

Type of Contact	☐ Phone Call/Text	☐ Email
	☐ Informal Meeting	☐ Letter/Note
	☐ Arranged Meeting	☐ Class Dojo
	☐ Other: _____	

Phone Call Response	☐ No Answer	☐ Wrong Number _____	☐ Left Voicemail	☐ Sent Text

Topic Discussed	☐ Grades	☐ Behavior
	☐ Homework	☐ Class work
	☐ Projects	☐ Schedule Meeting
Notes/Other:		

Action to be Taken:

Contact Purpose	☐ Glow	☐ Grow

Try to be a rainbow in someone else's cloud. — *Maya Angelou.*

Contact Documentation Form

Student Name: _____   Class: _____

Date and Time: _____   Person Initiating: _____

Person Contacted	□ Parent/Guardian:
	□ Counselor:
	□ Nurse:
	□ Administrator:
	□ Other:

Type of Contact	□ Phone Call/Text	□ Email
	□ Informal Meeting	□ Letter/Note
	□ Arranged Meeting	□ Class Dojo
	□ Other: _____	

Phone Call Response	□ No Answer	□ Wrong Number _____	□ Left Voicemail	□ Sent Text

Topic Discussed	□ Grades	□ Behavior
	□ Homework	□ Class work
	□ Projects	□ Schedule Meeting
Notes/Other:		

Action to be Taken:

Contact Purpose	□ Glow	□ Grow

You are enough just as you are. — Megan Markle

Contact Documentation Form

Student Name: _____ Class: _____

Date and Time: _____ Person Initiating: _____

Person Contacted	☐ Parent/Guardian:
	☐ Counselor:
	☐ Nurse:
	☐ Administrator:
	☐ Other:

Type of Contact	☐ Phone Call/Text	☐ Email
	☐ Informal Meeting	☐ Letter/Note
	☐ Arranged Meeting	☐ Class Dojo
	☐ Other: _____	

Phone Call Response	☐ No Answer	☐ Wrong Number _____	☐ Left Voicemail	☐ Sent Text

Topic Discussed	☐ Grades	☐ Behavior
	☐ Homework	☐ Class work
	☐ Projects	☐ Schedule Meeting
Notes/Other:		

Action to be Taken:

Contact Purpose	☐ Glow	☐ Grow

Leadership is about making others better as a result of your presence and making sure that impact lasts in your absence. - Unknown

Contact Documentation Form

Student Name: _____   Class: _____

Date and Time: _____   Person Initiating: _____

Person Contacted	□ Parent/Guardian:
	□ Counselor:
	□ Nurse:
	□ Administrator:
	□ Other:

Type of Contact	□ Phone Call/Text	□ Email
	□ Informal Meeting	□ Letter/Note
	□ Arranged Meeting	□ Class Dojo
	□ Other: _____	

Phone Call Response	□ No Answer	□ Wrong Number _____	□ Left Voicemail	□ Sent Text

Topic Discussed	□ Grades	□ Behavior
	□ Homework	□ Class work
	□ Projects	□ Schedule Meeting
Notes/Other:		

Action to be Taken:

Contact Purpose	□ Glow	□ Grow

Be a Pineapple. Stand tall. Wear a Crown, and Be sweet on the inside. - Unknown

Contact Documentation Form

Student Name: _____   Class: _____

Date and Time: _____   Person Initiating: _____

Person Contacted	☐ Parent/Guardian:
	☐ Counselor:
	☐ Nurse:
	☐ Administrator:
	☐ Other:

Type of Contact	☐ Phone Call/Text	☐ Email
	☐ Informal Meeting	☐ Letter/Note
	☐ Arranged Meeting	☐ Class Dojo
	☐ Other: _____	

Phone Call Response	☐ No Answer	☐ Wrong Number _____	☐ Left Voicemail	☐ Sent Text

Topic Discussed	☐ Grades	☐ Behavior
	☐ Homework	☐ Class work
	☐ Projects	☐ Schedule Meeting
Notes/Other:		

Action to be Taken:

Contact Purpose	☐ Glow	☐ Grow

The first step to getting somewhere is to decide you're not going to stay where you are. – J.P. Morgan

Contact Documentation Form

Student Name: _____   Class: _____

Date and Time: _____   Person Initiating: _____

Person Contacted	☐ Parent/Guardian:
	☐ Counselor:
	☐ Nurse:
	☐ Administrator:
	☐ Other:

Type of Contact	☐ Phone Call/Text	☐ Email
	☐ Informal Meeting	☐ Letter/Note
	☐ Arranged Meeting	☐ Class Dojo
	☐ Other: _____	

Phone Call Response	☐ No Answer	☐ Wrong Number _____	☐ Left Voicemail	☐ Sent Text

Topic Discussed	☐ Grades	☐ Behavior
	☐ Homework	☐ Class work
	☐ Projects	☐ Schedule Meeting
Notes/Other:		

Action to be Taken:

Contact Purpose	☐ Glow	☐ Grow

You can't go back and change the beginning but you can start where you are and change the ending. – C.S. Lewis

Contact Documentation Form

Student Name: _____   Class: _____

Date and Time: _____   Person Initiating: _____

Person Contacted	☐ Parent/Guardian:
	☐ Counselor:
	☐ Nurse:
	☐ Administrator:
	☐ Other:

Type of Contact	☐ Phone Call/Text	☐ Email
	☐ Informal Meeting	☐ Letter/Note
	☐ Arranged Meeting	☐ Class Dojo
	☐ Other: _____	

Phone Call Response	☐ No Answer	☐ Wrong Number _____	☐ Left Voicemail	☐ Sent Text

Topic Discussed	☐ Grades	☐ Behavior
	☐ Homework	☐ Class work
	☐ Projects	☐ Schedule Meeting
Notes/Other:		

Action to be Taken:

Contact Purpose	☐ Glow	☐ Grow

Believe in yourself a little more.

Contact Documentation Form

Student Name: _____ Class: _____

Date and Time: _____ Person Initiating: _____

Person Contacted	☐ Parent/Guardian:
	☐ Counselor:
	☐ Nurse:
	☐ Administrator:
	☐ Other:

Type of Contact	☐ Phone Call/Text	☐ Email
	☐ Informal Meeting	☐ Letter/Note
	☐ Arranged Meeting	☐ Class Dojo
	☐ Other: _____	

Phone Call Response	☐ No Answer	☐ Wrong Number _____	☐ Left Voicemail	☐ Sent Text

Topic Discussed	☐ Grades	☐ Behavior
	☐ Homework	☐ Class work
	☐ Projects	☐ Schedule Meeting
Notes/Other:		

Action to be Taken:

Contact Purpose	☐ Glow	☐ Grow

There is only one corner of the universe you can be certain improving and that's your own self.

-Aldous Huxley

Contact Documentation Form

Student Name: _____ Class: _____

Date and Time: _____ Person Initiating: _____

Person Contacted	□ Parent/Guardian:
	□ Counselor:
	□ Nurse:
	□ Administrator:
	□ Other:

Type of Contact	□ Phone Call/Text	□ Email
	□ Informal Meeting	□ Letter/Note
	□ Arranged Meeting	□ Class Dojo
	□ Other: _____	

Phone Call Response	□ No Answer	□ Wrong Number _____	□ Left Voicemail	□ Sent Text

Topic Discussed	□ Grades	□ Behavior
	□ Homework	□ Class work
	□ Projects	□ Schedule Meeting
Notes/Other:		

Action to be Taken:

Contact Purpose	□ Glow	□ Grow

A thousand mistakes are an education if you learn something from every one of them.

Contact Documentation Form

Student Name: _____   Class: _____

Date and Time: _____   Person Initiating: _____

Person Contacted	□ Parent/Guardian:
	□ Counselor:
	□ Nurse:
	□ Administrator:
	□ Other:

Type of Contact	□ Phone Call/Text	□ Email
	□ Informal Meeting	□ Letter/Note
	□ Arranged Meeting	□ Class Dojo
	□ Other: _____	

Phone Call Response	□ No Answer	□ Wrong Number _____	□ Left Voicemail	□ Sent Text

Topic Discussed	□ Grades	□ Behavior
	□ Homework	□ Class work
	□ Projects	□ Schedule Meeting
Notes/Other:		

Action to be Taken:

Contact Purpose	□ Glow	□ Grow

I can. I will. End of story.

Contact Documentation Form

Student Name: _____   Class: _____

Date and Time: _____   Person Initiating: _____

Person Contacted	☐ Parent/Guardian:
	☐ Counselor:
	☐ Nurse:
	☐ Administrator:
	☐ Other:

Type of Contact	☐ Phone Call/Text	☐ Email
	☐ Informal Meeting	☐ Letter/Note
	☐ Arranged Meeting	☐ Class Dojo
	☐ Other: _____	

Phone Call Response	☐ No Answer	☐ Wrong Number _____	☐ Left Voicemail	☐ Sent Text

Topic Discussed	☐ Grades	☐ Behavior
	☐ Homework	☐ Class work
	☐ Projects	☐ Schedule Meeting
Notes/Other:		

Action to be Taken:

Contact Purpose	☐ Glow	☐ Grow

You are capable of amazing things.

Contact Documentation Form

Student Name: _____   Class: _____

Date and Time: _____   Person Initiating: _____

Person Contacted	□ Parent/Guardian:
	□ Counselor:
	□ Nurse:
	□ Administrator:
	□ Other:

Type of Contact	□ Phone Call/Text	□ Email
	□ Informal Meeting	□ Letter/Note
	□ Arranged Meeting	□ Class Dojo
	□ Other: _____	

Phone Call Response	□ No Answer	□ Wrong Number _____	□ Left Voicemail	□ Sent Text

Topic Discussed	□ Grades	□ Behavior
	□ Homework	□ Class work
	□ Projects	□ Schedule Meeting

Notes/Other:

Action to be Taken:

Contact Purpose	□ Glow	□ Grow

Be careful how you are talking to yourself because you are listening.

Contact Documentation Form

Student Name: _____ Class: _____

Date and Time: _____ Person Initiating: _____

Person Contacted	☐ Parent/Guardian:
	☐ Counselor:
	☐ Nurse:
	☐ Administrator:
	☐ Other:

Type of Contact	☐ Phone Call/Text	☐ Email
	☐ Informal Meeting	☐ Letter/Note
	☐ Arranged Meeting	☐ Class Dojo
	☐ Other: _____	

Phone Call Response	☐ No Answer	☐ Wrong Number _____	☐ Left Voicemail	☐ Sent Text

Topic Discussed	☐ Grades	☐ Behavior
	☐ Homework	☐ Class work
	☐ Projects	☐ Schedule Meeting
Notes/Other:		

Action to be Taken:

Contact Purpose	☐ Glow	☐ Grow

I'm too busy working on my own grass to notice if yours is greener.

Contact Documentation Form

Student Name: _____   Class: _____

Date and Time: _____   Person Initiating: _____

Person Contacted	□ Parent/Guardian:
	□ Counselor:
	□ Nurse:
	□ Administrator:
	□ Other:

Type of Contact	□ Phone Call/Text	□ Email
	□ Informal Meeting	□ Letter/Note
	□ Arranged Meeting	□ Class Dojo
	□ Other: _____	

Phone Call Response	□ No Answer	□ Wrong Number _____	□ Left Voicemail	□ Sent Text

Topic Discussed	□ Grades	□ Behavior
	□ Homework	□ Class work
	□ Projects	□ Schedule Meeting
Notes/Other:		

Action to be Taken:

Contact Purpose	□ Glow	□ Grow

You can totally do this!!

Contact Documentation Form

Student Name: _____   Class: _____

Date and Time: _____   Person Initiating: _____

Person Contacted	☐ Parent/Guardian:
	☐ Counselor:
	☐ Nurse:
	☐ Administrator:
	☐ Other:

Type of Contact	☐ Phone Call/Text	☐ Email
	☐ Informal Meeting	☐ Letter/Note
	☐ Arranged Meeting	☐ Class Dojo
	☐ Other: _____	

Phone Call Response	☐ No Answer	☐ Wrong Number _____	☐ Left Voicemail	☐ Sent Text

Topic Discussed	☐ Grades	☐ Behavior
	☐ Homework	☐ Class work
	☐ Projects	☐ Schedule Meeting
Notes/Other:		

Action to be Taken:

Contact Purpose	☐ Glow	☐ Grow

No pressure. No diamonds.

Contact Documentation Form

Student Name: _____   Class: _____

Date and Time: _____   Person Initiating: _____

Person Contacted	□ Parent/Guardian:
	□ Counselor:
	□ Nurse:
	□ Administrator:
	□ Other:

Type of Contact	□ Phone Call/Text	□ Email
	□ Informal Meeting	□ Letter/Note
	□ Arranged Meeting	□ Class Dojo
	□ Other: _____	

Phone Call Response	□ No Answer	□ Wrong Number _____	□ Left Voicemail	□ Sent Text

Topic Discussed	□ Grades	□ Behavior
	□ Homework	□ Class work
	□ Projects	□ Schedule Meeting
Notes/Other:		

Action to be Taken:

Contact Purpose	□ Glow	□ Grow

Life is better when you're laughing...

Contact Documentation Form

Student Name: _____ Class: _____

Date and Time: _____ Person Initiating: _____

Person Contacted	☐ Parent/Guardian:
	☐ Counselor:
	☐ Nurse:
	☐ Administrator:
	☐ Other:

Type of Contact	☐ Phone Call/Text	☐ Email
	☐ Informal Meeting	☐ Letter/Note
	☐ Arranged Meeting	☐ Class Dojo
	☐ Other: _____	

Phone Call Response	☐ No Answer	☐ Wrong Number _____	☐ Left Voicemail	☐ Sent Text

Topic Discussed	☐ Grades	☐ Behavior
	☐ Homework	☐ Class work
	☐ Projects	☐ Schedule Meeting
Notes/Other:		

Action to be Taken:

Contact Purpose	☐ Glow	☐ Grow

If you want to fly, give up everything that weighs you down. - Budhha

Contact Documentation Form

Student Name: _____ Class: _____

Date and Time: _____ Person Initiating: _____

Person Contacted	□ Parent/Guardian:
	□ Counselor:
	□ Nurse:
	□ Administrator:
	□ Other:

Type of Contact	□ Phone Call/Text	□ Email
	□ Informal Meeting	□ Letter/Note
	□ Arranged Meeting	□ Class Dojo
	□ Other: _____	

Phone Call Response	□ No Answer	□ Wrong Number _____	□ Left Voicemail	□ Sent Text

Topic Discussed	□ Grades	□ Behavior
	□ Homework	□ Class work
	□ Projects	□ Schedule Meeting
Notes/Other:		

Action to be Taken:

Contact Purpose	□ Glow	□ Grow

A smart person knows what to say; a wise person knows whether or not to say it.

Contact Documentation Form

Student Name: _____   Class: _____

Date and Time: _____   Person Initiating: _____

Person Contacted	☐ Parent/Guardian:
	☐ Counselor:
	☐ Nurse:
	☐ Administrator:
	☐ Other:

Type of Contact	☐ Phone Call/Text	☐ Email
	☐ Informal Meeting	☐ Letter/Note
	☐ Arranged Meeting	☐ Class Dojo
	☐ Other: _____	

Phone Call Response	☐ No Answer	☐ Wrong Number _____	☐ Left Voicemail	☐ Sent Text

Topic Discussed	☐ Grades	☐ Behavior
	☐ Homework	☐ Class work
	☐ Projects	☐ Schedule Meeting
Notes/Other:		

Action to be Taken:

Contact Purpose	☐ Glow	☐ Grow

Count your blessings. Name them one by one and see what the Lord has done.

Contact Documentation Form

Student Name: _____   Class: _____

Date and Time: _____   Person Initiating: _____

Person Contacted	□ Parent/Guardian:
	□ Counselor:
	□ Nurse:
	□ Administrator:
	□ Other:

Type of Contact	□ Phone Call/Text	□ Email
	□ Informal Meeting	□ Letter/Note
	□ Arranged Meeting	□ Class Dojo
	□ Other: _____	

Phone Call Response	□ No Answer	□ Wrong Number _____	□ Left Voicemail	□ Sent Text

Topic Discussed	□ Grades	□ Behavior
	□ Homework	□ Class work
	□ Projects	□ Schedule Meeting
Notes/Other:		

Action to be Taken:

Contact Purpose	□ Glow	□ Grow

No rain. No flowers.

Contact Documentation Form

Student Name: _____ Class: _____

Date and Time: _____ Person Initiating: _____

Person Contacted	□ Parent/Guardian:	
	□ Counselor:	
	□ Nurse:	
	□ Administrator:	
	□ Other:	

Type of Contact	□ Phone Call/Text	□ Email
	□ Informal Meeting	□ Letter/Note
	□ Arranged Meeting	□ Class Dojo
	□ Other: _____	

Phone Call Response	□ No Answer	□ Wrong Number _____	□ Left Voicemail	□ Sent Text

Topic Discussed	□ Grades	□ Behavior
	□ Homework	□ Class work
	□ Projects	□ Schedule Meeting
Notes/Other:		

Action to be Taken:

Contact Purpose	□ Glow	□ Grow

NEVER DULL YOUR SUNSHINE FOR SOMEONE ELSE.

Contact Documentation Form

Student Name: _____   Class: _____

Date and Time: _____   Person Initiating: _____

Person Contacted	☐ Parent/Guardian:
	☐ Counselor:
	☐ Nurse:
	☐ Administrator:
	☐ Other:

Type of Contact	☐ Phone Call/Text	☐ Email
	☐ Informal Meeting	☐ Letter/Note
	☐ Arranged Meeting	☐ Class Dojo
	☐ Other: _____	

Phone Call Response	☐ No Answer	☐ Wrong Number _____	☐ Left Voicemail	☐ Sent Text

Topic Discussed	☐ Grades	☐ Behavior
	☐ Homework	☐ Class work
	☐ Projects	☐ Schedule Meeting
Notes/Other:		

Action to be Taken:

Contact Purpose	☐ Glow	☐ Grow

Life is too short to wait until tomorrow.

Contact Documentation Form

Student Name: _____   Class: _____

Date and Time: _____   Person Initiating: _____

Person Contacted	☐ Parent/Guardian:
	☐ Counselor:
	☐ Nurse:
	☐ Administrator:
	☐ Other:

Type of Contact	☐ Phone Call/Text	☐ Email
	☐ Informal Meeting	☐ Letter/Note
	☐ Arranged Meeting	☐ Class Dojo
	☐ Other: _____	

Phone Call Response	☐ No Answer	☐ Wrong Number _____	☐ Left Voicemail	☐ Sent Text

Topic Discussed	☐ Grades	☐ Behavior
	☐ Homework	☐ Class work
	☐ Projects	☐ Schedule Meeting
Notes/Other:		

Action to be Taken:

Contact Purpose	☐ Glow	☐ Grow

Life is a onetime offer. Use it well.

Contact Documentation Form

Student Name: _____   Class: _____

Date and Time: _____   Person Initiating: _____

Person Contacted	
	□ Parent/Guardian:
	□ Counselor:
	□ Nurse:
	□ Administrator:
	□ Other:

Type of Contact		
	□ Phone Call/Text	□ Email
	□ Informal Meeting	□ Letter/Note
	□ Arranged Meeting	□ Class Dojo
	□ Other: _____	

Phone Call Response	□ No Answer	□ Wrong Number _____	□ Left Voicemail	□ Sent Text

Topic Discussed		
	□ Grades	□ Behavior
	□ Homework	□ Class work
	□ Projects	□ Schedule Meeting
Notes/Other:		

Action to be Taken:

Contact Purpose	□ Glow	□ Grow

Nothing changes if nothing changes.

Contact Documentation Form

Student Name: _____ Class: _____

Date and Time: _____ Person Initiating: _____

Person Contacted	☐ Parent/Guardian:
	☐ Counselor:
	☐ Nurse:
	☐ Administrator:
	☐ Other:

Type of Contact	☐ Phone Call/Text	☐ Email
	☐ Informal Meeting	☐ Letter/Note
	☐ Arranged Meeting	☐ Class Dojo
	☐ Other: _____	

Phone Call Response	☐ No Answer	☐ Wrong Number _____	☐ Left Voicemail	☐ Sent Text

Topic Discussed	☐ Grades	☐ Behavior
	☐ Homework	☐ Class work
	☐ Projects	☐ Schedule Meeting
Notes/Other:		

Action to be Taken:

Contact Purpose	☐ Glow	☐ Grow

Sometimes you have to keep good news to yourself. Everybody is not genuinely happy for you.

Contact Documentation Form

Student Name: _____   Class: _____

Date and Time: _____   Person Initiating: _____

Person Contacted	□ Parent/Guardian:
	□ Counselor:
	□ Nurse:
	□ Administrator:
	□ Other:

Type of Contact	□ Phone Call/Text	□ Email
	□ Informal Meeting	□ Letter/Note
	□ Arranged Meeting	□ Class Dojo
	□ Other: _____	

Phone Call Response	□ No Answer	□ Wrong Number _____	□ Left Voicemail	□ Sent Text

Topic Discussed	□ Grades	□ Behavior
	□ Homework	□ Class work
	□ Projects	□ Schedule Meeting
Notes/Other:		

Action to be Taken:

Contact Purpose	□ Glow	□ Grow

If someone doesn't appreciate your presence, make them appreciate your absence.

Contact Documentation Form

Student Name: _____ Class: _____

Date and Time: _____ Person Initiating: _____

Person Contacted	☐ Parent/Guardian:
	☐ Counselor:
	☐ Nurse:
	☐ Administrator:
	☐ Other:

Type of Contact	☐ Phone Call/Text	☐ Email
	☐ Informal Meeting	☐ Letter/Note
	☐ Arranged Meeting	☐ Class Dojo
	☐ Other: _____	

Phone Call Response	☐ No Answer	☐ Wrong Number _____	☐ Left Voicemail	☐ Sent Text

Topic Discussed	☐ Grades	☐ Behavior
	☐ Homework	☐ Class work
	☐ Projects	☐ Schedule Meeting
Notes/Other:		

Action to be Taken:

Contact Purpose	☐ Glow	☐ Grow

Do more of what makes you happy.

Contact Documentation Form

Student Name: _____   Class: _____

Date and Time: _____   Person Initiating: _____

Person Contacted	☐ Parent/Guardian:
	☐ Counselor:
	☐ Nurse:
	☐ Administrator:
	☐ Other:

Type of Contact	☐ Phone Call/Text	☐ Email
	☐ Informal Meeting	☐ Letter/Note
	☐ Arranged Meeting	☐ Class Dojo
	☐ Other: _____	

Phone Call Response	☐ No Answer	☐ Wrong Number _____	☐ Left Voicemail	☐ Sent Text

Topic Discussed	☐ Grades	☐ Behavior
	☐ Homework	☐ Class work
	☐ Projects	☐ Schedule Meeting
Notes/Other:		

Action to be Taken:

Contact Purpose	☐ Glow	☐ Grow

Every master was once a beginner.

Contact Documentation Form

Student Name: _____   Class: _____

Date and Time: _____   Person Initiating: _____

Person Contacted	□ Parent/Guardian:
	□ Counselor:
	□ Nurse:
	□ Administrator:
	□ Other:

Type of Contact	□ Phone Call/Text	□ Email
	□ Informal Meeting	□ Letter/Note
	□ Arranged Meeting	□ Class Dojo
	□ Other: _____	

Phone Call Response	□ No Answer	□ Wrong Number _____	□ Left Voicemail	□ Sent Text

Topic Discussed	□ Grades	□ Behavior
	□ Homework	□ Class work
	□ Projects	□ Schedule Meeting
Notes/Other:		

Action to be Taken:

Contact Purpose	□ Glow	□ Grow

Don't hold on to thoughts that don't allow your mind to move forward.

Contact Documentation Form

Student Name: _____   Class: _____

Date and Time: _____   Person Initiating: _____

Person Contacted	☐ Parent/Guardian:
	☐ Counselor:
	☐ Nurse:
	☐ Administrator:
	☐ Other:

Type of Contact	☐ Phone Call/Text	☐ Email
	☐ Informal Meeting	☐ Letter/Note
	☐ Arranged Meeting	☐ Class Dojo
	☐ Other: _____	

Phone Call Response	☐ No Answer	☐ Wrong Number _____	☐ Left Voicemail	☐ Sent Text

Topic Discussed	☐ Grades	☐ Behavior
	☐ Homework	☐ Class work
	☐ Projects	☐ Schedule Meeting
Notes/Other:		

Action to be Taken:

Contact Purpose	☐ Glow	☐ Grow

NOTE TO SELF: STOP TRYING SO HARD FOR PEOPLE WHO DON'T CARE.

Contact Documentation Form

Student Name: _____   Class: _____

Date and Time: _____   Person Initiating: _____

Person Contacted	☐ Parent/Guardian:
	☐ Counselor:
	☐ Nurse:
	☐ Administrator:
	☐ Other:

Type of Contact	☐ Phone Call/Text	☐ Email
	☐ Informal Meeting	☐ Letter/Note
	☐ Arranged Meeting	☐ Class Dojo
	☐ Other: _____	

Phone Call Response	☐ No Answer	☐ Wrong Number _____	☐ Left Voicemail	☐ Sent Text

Topic Discussed	☐ Grades	☐ Behavior
	☐ Homework	☐ Class work
	☐ Projects	☐ Schedule Meeting
Notes/Other:		

Action to be Taken:

Contact Purpose	☐ Glow	☐ Grow

Many a false step is made by standing still.

Contact Documentation Form

Student Name: _____   Class: _____

Date and Time: _____   Person Initiating: _____

Person Contacted	□ Parent/Guardian:
	□ Counselor:
	□ Nurse:
	□ Administrator:
	□ Other:

Type of Contact	□ Phone Call/Text	□ Email
	□ Informal Meeting	□ Letter/Note
	□ Arranged Meeting	□ Class Dojo
	□ Other: _____	

Phone Call Response	□ No Answer	□ Wrong Number _____	□ Left Voicemail	□ Sent Text

Topic Discussed	□ Grades	□ Behavior
	□ Homework	□ Class work
	□ Projects	□ Schedule Meeting
Notes/Other:		

Action to be Taken:

Contact Purpose	□ Glow	□ Grow

Know God, Know Peace.

Contact Documentation Form

Student Name: _____ Class: _____

Date and Time: _____ Person Initiating: _____

Person Contacted	□ Parent/Guardian:
	□ Counselor:
	□ Nurse:
	□ Administrator:
	□ Other:

Type of Contact	□ Phone Call/Text	□ Email
	□ Informal Meeting	□ Letter/Note
	□ Arranged Meeting	□ Class Dojo
	□ Other: _____	

Phone Call Response	□ No Answer	□ Wrong Number _____	□ Left Voicemail	□ Sent Text

Topic Discussed	□ Grades	□ Behavior
	□ Homework	□ Class work
	□ Projects	□ Schedule Meeting
Notes/Other:		

Action to be Taken:

Contact Purpose	□ Glow	□ Grow

Accept everything you are and nothing you are not.

Contact Documentation Form

Student Name: _____ Class: _____

Date and Time: _____ Person Initiating: _____

Person Contacted	☐ Parent/Guardian:
	☐ Counselor:
	☐ Nurse:
	☐ Administrator:
	☐ Other:

Type of Contact	☐ Phone Call/Text	☐ Email
	☐ Informal Meeting	☐ Letter/Note
	☐ Arranged Meeting	☐ Class Dojo
	☐ Other: _____	

Phone Call Response	☐ No Answer	☐ Wrong Number _____	☐ Left Voicemail	☐ Sent Text

Topic Discussed	☐ Grades	☐ Behavior
	☐ Homework	☐ Class work
	☐ Projects	☐ Schedule Meeting
Notes/Other:		

Action to be Taken:

Contact Purpose	☐ Glow	☐ Grow

This will make perfect sense one day.

Contact Documentation Form

Student Name: _____   Class: _____

Date and Time: _____   Person Initiating: _____

Person Contacted	☐ Parent/Guardian:
	☐ Counselor:
	☐ Nurse:
	☐ Administrator:
	☐ Other:

Type of Contact	☐ Phone Call/Text	☐ Email
	☐ Informal Meeting	☐ Letter/Note
	☐ Arranged Meeting	☐ Class Dojo
	☐ Other: _____	

Phone Call Response	☐ No Answer	☐ Wrong Number _____	☐ Left Voicemail	☐ Sent Text

Topic Discussed	☐ Grades	☐ Behavior
	☐ Homework	☐ Class work
	☐ Projects	☐ Schedule Meeting
Notes/Other:		

Action to be Taken:

Contact Purpose	☐ Glow	☐ Grow

Remember to live.

Contact Documentation Form

Student Name: _____   Class: _____

Date and Time: _____   Person Initiating: _____

Person Contacted	□ Parent/Guardian:
	□ Counselor:
	□ Nurse:
	□ Administrator:
	□ Other:

Type of Contact	□ Phone Call/Text	□ Email
	□ Informal Meeting	□ Letter/Note
	□ Arranged Meeting	□ Class Dojo
	□ Other: _____	

Phone Call Response	□ No Answer	□ Wrong Number _____	□ Left Voicemail	□ Sent Text

Topic Discussed	□ Grades	□ Behavior
	□ Homework	□ Class work
	□ Projects	□ Schedule Meeting
Notes/Other:		

Action to be Taken:

Contact Purpose	□ Glow	□ Grow

It's okay if the only thing you did today was breathe.

Contact Documentation Form

Student Name: _____   Class: _____

Date and Time: _____   Person Initiating: _____

Person Contacted	☐ Parent/Guardian:
	☐ Counselor:
	☐ Nurse:
	☐ Administrator:
	☐ Other:

Type of Contact	☐ Phone Call/Text	☐ Email
	☐ Informal Meeting	☐ Letter/Note
	☐ Arranged Meeting	☐ Class Dojo
	☐ Other: _____	

Phone Call Response	☐ No Answer	☐ Wrong Number _____	☐ Left Voicemail	☐ Sent Text

Topic Discussed	☐ Grades	☐ Behavior
	☐ Homework	☐ Class work
	☐ Projects	☐ Schedule Meeting
Notes/Other:		

Action to be Taken:

Contact Purpose	☐ Glow	☐ Grow

Be selective in your battles. Sometimes peace is better than being right.

Contact Documentation Form

Student Name: _____ Class: _____

Date and Time: _____ Person Initiating: _____

Person Contacted	□ Parent/Guardian:
	□ Counselor:
	□ Nurse:
	□ Administrator:
	□ Other:

Type of Contact	□ Phone Call/Text	□ Email
	□ Informal Meeting	□ Letter/Note
	□ Arranged Meeting	□ Class Dojo
	□ Other: _____	

Phone Call Response	□ No Answer	□ Wrong Number _____	□ Left Voicemail	□ Sent Text

Topic Discussed	□ Grades	□ Behavior
	□ Homework	□ Class work
	□ Projects	□ Schedule Meeting
Notes/Other:		

Action to be Taken:

Contact Purpose	□ Glow	□ Grow

Why follow when you can LEAD.

Contact Documentation Form

Student Name: _____ Class: _____

Date and Time: _____ Person Initiating: _____

Person Contacted	□ Parent/Guardian:
	□ Counselor:
	□ Nurse:
	□ Administrator:
	□ Other:

Type of Contact	□ Phone Call/Text	□ Email
	□ Informal Meeting	□ Letter/Note
	□ Arranged Meeting	□ Class Dojo
	□ Other: _____	

Phone Call Response	□ No Answer	□ Wrong Number _____	□ Left Voicemail	□ Sent Text

Topic Discussed	□ Grades	□ Behavior
	□ Homework	□ Class work
	□ Projects	□ Schedule Meeting
Notes/Other:		

Action to be Taken:

Contact Purpose	□ Glow	□ Grow

Carpe Diem.

Contact Documentation Form

Student Name: _____   Class: _____

Date and Time: _____   Person Initiating: _____

Person Contacted	☐ Parent/Guardian:
	☐ Counselor:
	☐ Nurse:
	☐ Administrator:
	☐ Other:

Type of Contact	☐ Phone Call/Text	☐ Email
	☐ Informal Meeting	☐ Letter/Note
	☐ Arranged Meeting	☐ Class Dojo
	☐ Other: _____	

Phone Call Response	☐ No Answer	☐ Wrong Number _____	☐ Left Voicemail	☐ Sent Text

Topic Discussed	☐ Grades	☐ Behavior
	☐ Homework	☐ Class work
	☐ Projects	☐ Schedule Meeting
Notes/Other:		

Action to be Taken:

Contact Purpose	☐ Glow	☐ Grow

Still I rise.

Contact Documentation Form

Student Name: _____   Class: _____

Date and Time: _____   Person Initiating: _____

Person Contacted	□ Parent/Guardian:
	□ Counselor:
	□ Nurse:
	□ Administrator:
	□ Other:

Type of Contact	□ Phone Call/Text	□ Email
	□ Informal Meeting	□ Letter/Note
	□ Arranged Meeting	□ Class Dojo
	□ Other: _____	

Phone Call Response	□ No Answer	□ Wrong Number _____	□ Left Voicemail	□ Sent Text

Topic Discussed	□ Grades	□ Behavior
	□ Homework	□ Class work
	□ Projects	□ Schedule Meeting
Notes/Other:		

Action to be Taken:

Contact Purpose	□ Glow	□ Grow

Coffee and kindness…maybe two coffees and then kindness.

Contact Documentation Form

Student Name: _____   Class: _____

Date and Time: _____   Person Initiating: _____

Person Contacted	☐ Parent/Guardian:
	☐ Counselor:
	☐ Nurse:
	☐ Administrator:
	☐ Other:

Type of Contact	☐ Phone Call/Text	☐ Email
	☐ Informal Meeting	☐ Letter/Note
	☐ Arranged Meeting	☐ Class Dojo
	☐ Other: _____	

Phone Call Response	☐ No Answer	☐ Wrong Number _____	☐ Left Voicemail	☐ Sent Text

Topic Discussed	☐ Grades	☐ Behavior
	☐ Homework	☐ Class work
	☐ Projects	☐ Schedule Meeting
Notes/Other:		

Action to be Taken:

Contact Purpose	☐ Glow	☐ Grow

THE DREAM IS FREE. THE HUSTLE IS SOLD SEPARATELY.

Contact Documentation Form

Student Name: _____ Class: _____

Date and Time: _____ Person Initiating: _____

Person Contacted	☐ Parent/Guardian:
	☐ Counselor:
	☐ Nurse:
	☐ Administrator:
	☐ Other:

Type of Contact	☐ Phone Call/Text	☐ Email
	☐ Informal Meeting	☐ Letter/Note
	☐ Arranged Meeting	☐ Class Dojo
	☐ Other: _____	

Phone Call Response	☐ No Answer	☐ Wrong Number _____	☐ Left Voicemail	☐ Sent Text

Topic Discussed	☐ Grades	☐ Behavior
	☐ Homework	☐ Class work
	☐ Projects	☐ Schedule Meeting
Notes/Other:		

Action to be Taken:

Contact Purpose	☐ Glow	☐ Grow

Stay strong. Your story isn't over yet.

Contact Documentation Form

Student Name: _____ Class: _____

Date and Time: _____ Person Initiating: _____

Person Contacted	□ Parent/Guardian:
	□ Counselor:
	□ Nurse:
	□ Administrator:
	□ Other:

Type of Contact	□ Phone Call/Text	□ Email
	□ Informal Meeting	□ Letter/Note
	□ Arranged Meeting	□ Class Dojo
	□ Other: _____	

Phone Call Response	□ No Answer	□ Wrong Number _____	□ Left Voicemail	□ Sent Text

Topic Discussed	□ Grades	□ Behavior
	□ Homework	□ Class work
	□ Projects	□ Schedule Meeting
Notes/Other:		

Action to be Taken:

Contact Purpose	□ Glow	□ Grow

Smile and walk away.

Contact Documentation Form

Student Name: _____   Class: _____

Date and Time: _____   Person Initiating: _____

Person Contacted	☐ Parent/Guardian:
	☐ Counselor:
	☐ Nurse:
	☐ Administrator:
	☐ Other:

Type of Contact	☐ Phone Call/Text	☐ Email
	☐ Informal Meeting	☐ Letter/Note
	☐ Arranged Meeting	☐ Class Dojo
	☐ Other: _____	

Phone Call Response	☐ No Answer	☐ Wrong Number _____	☐ Left Voicemail	☐ Sent Text

Topic Discussed	☐ Grades	☐ Behavior
	☐ Homework	☐ Class work
	☐ Projects	☐ Schedule Meeting
Notes/Other:		

Action to be Taken:

Contact Purpose	☐ Glow	☐ Grow

Let gratitude be your attitude.

Contact Documentation Form

Student Name: _____   Class: _____

Date and Time: _____   Person Initiating: _____

Person Contacted	☐ Parent/Guardian:
	☐ Counselor:
	☐ Nurse:
	☐ Administrator:
	☐ Other:

Type of Contact	☐ Phone Call/Text	☐ Email
	☐ Informal Meeting	☐ Letter/Note
	☐ Arranged Meeting	☐ Class Dojo
	☐ Other: _____	

Phone Call Response	☐ No Answer	☐ Wrong Number _____	☐ Left Voicemail	☐ Sent Text

Topic Discussed	☐ Grades	☐ Behavior
	☐ Homework	☐ Class work
	☐ Projects	☐ Schedule Meeting
Notes/Other:		

Action to be Taken:

Contact Purpose	☐ Glow	☐ Grow

If you want the rainbow, you have to deal with the rain.

Contact Documentation Form

Student Name: _____   Class: _____

Date and Time: _____   Person Initiating: _____

Person Contacted	☐ Parent/Guardian:
	☐ Counselor:
	☐ Nurse:
	☐ Administrator:
	☐ Other:

Type of Contact	☐ Phone Call/Text	☐ Email
	☐ Informal Meeting	☐ Letter/Note
	☐ Arranged Meeting	☐ Class Dojo
	☐ Other: _____	

Phone Call Response	☐ No Answer	☐ Wrong Number _____	☐ Left Voicemail	☐ Sent Text

Topic Discussed	☐ Grades	☐ Behavior
	☐ Homework	☐ Class work
	☐ Projects	☐ Schedule Meeting
Notes/Other:		

Action to be Taken:

Contact Purpose	☐ Glow	☐ Grow

But God!

School Year

_____

Contact Documentation Form

Student Name: _____ Class: _____

Date and Time: _____ Person Initiating: _____

Person Contacted	□ Parent/Guardian:
	□ Counselor:
	□ Nurse:
	□ Administrator:
	□ Other:

Type of Contact	□ Phone Call/Text	□ Email
	□ Informal Meeting	□ Letter/Note
	□ Arranged Meeting	□ Class Dojo
	□ Other: _____	

Phone Call Response	□ No Answer	□ Wrong Number _____	□ Left Voicemail	□ Sent Text

Topic Discussed	□ Grades	□ Behavior
	□ Homework	□ Class work
	□ Projects	□ Schedule Meeting
Notes/Other:		

Action to be Taken:

Contact Purpose	□ Glow	□ Grow

Out of a mountain of despair, a stone of hope. — Martin Luther King, Jr.

Contact Documentation Form

Student Name: _____   Class: _____

Date and Time: _____   Person Initiating: _____

Person Contacted	☐ Parent/Guardian:
	☐ Counselor:
	☐ Nurse:
	☐ Administrator:
	☐ Other:

Type of Contact	☐ Phone Call/Text	☐ Email
	☐ Informal Meeting	☐ Letter/Note
	☐ Arranged Meeting	☐ Class Dojo
	☐ Other: _____	

Phone Call Response	☐ No Answer	☐ Wrong Number _____	☐ Left Voicemail	☐ Sent Text

Topic Discussed	☐ Grades	☐ Behavior
	☐ Homework	☐ Class work
	☐ Projects	☐ Schedule Meeting
Notes/Other:		

Action to be Taken:

Contact Purpose	☐ Glow	☐ Grow

Life has 2 rules. #1-Never Quit #2-Always remember rule #1 – Unknown

Contact Documentation Form

Student Name: _____   Class: _____

Date and Time: _____   Person Initiating: _____

Person Contacted	☐ Parent/Guardian:	
	☐ Counselor:	
	☐ Nurse:	
	☐ Administrator:	
	☐ Other:	

Type of Contact	☐ Phone Call/Text	☐ Email
	☐ Informal Meeting	☐ Letter/Note
	☐ Arranged Meeting	☐ Class Dojo
	☐ Other: _____	

Phone Call Response	☐ No Answer	☐ Wrong Number _____	☐ Left Voicemail	☐ Sent Text

Topic Discussed	☐ Grades	☐ Behavior
	☐ Homework	☐ Class work
	☐ Projects	☐ Schedule Meeting
Notes/Other:		

Action to be Taken:

Contact Purpose	☐ Glow	☐ Grow

Act as if what you do makes a difference. IT DOES. – *William James*

Contact Documentation Form

Student Name: _____   Class: _____

Date and Time: _____   Person Initiating: _____

Person Contacted	☐ Parent/Guardian:
	☐ Counselor:
	☐ Nurse:
	☐ Administrator:
	☐ Other:

Type of Contact	☐ Phone Call/Text	☐ Email
	☐ Informal Meeting	☐ Letter/Note
	☐ Arranged Meeting	☐ Class Dojo
	☐ Other: _____	

Phone Call Response	☐ No Answer	☐ Wrong Number _____	☐ Left Voicemail	☐ Sent Text

Topic Discussed	☐ Grades	☐ Behavior
	☐ Homework	☐ Class work
	☐ Projects	☐ Schedule Meeting
Notes/Other:		

Action to be Taken:

Contact Purpose	☐ Glow	☐ Grow

Nothing is impossible. The word itself says "I'm possible!" – *Audrey Hepburn*

Contact Documentation Form

Student Name: _____   Class: _____

Date and Time: _____   Person Initiating: _____

Person Contacted	□ Parent/Guardian:
	□ Counselor:
	□ Nurse:
	□ Administrator:
	□ Other:

Type of Contact	□ Phone Call/Text	□ Email
	□ Informal Meeting	□ Letter/Note
	□ Arranged Meeting	□ Class Dojo
	□ Other: _____	

Phone Call Response	□ No Answer	□ Wrong Number _____	□ Left Voicemail	□ Sent Text

Topic Discussed	□ Grades	□ Behavior
	□ Homework	□ Class work
	□ Projects	□ Schedule Meeting
Notes/Other:		

Action to be Taken:

Contact Purpose	□ Glow	□ Grow

Try to be a rainbow in someone else's cloud. — *Maya Angelou.*

Contact Documentation Form

Student Name: _____ Class: _____

Date and Time: _____ Person Initiating: _____

Person Contacted	☐ Parent/Guardian:
	☐ Counselor:
	☐ Nurse:
	☐ Administrator:
	☐ Other:

Type of Contact	☐ Phone Call/Text	☐ Email
	☐ Informal Meeting	☐ Letter/Note
	☐ Arranged Meeting	☐ Class Dojo
	☐ Other: _____	

Phone Call Response	☐ No Answer	☐ Wrong Number _____	☐ Left Voicemail	☐ Sent Text

Topic Discussed	☐ Grades	☐ Behavior
	☐ Homework	☐ Class work
	☐ Projects	☐ Schedule Meeting
Notes/Other:		

Action to be Taken:

Contact Purpose	☐ Glow	☐ Grow

Leadership is about making others better as a result of your presence and making sure that impact lasts in your absence. - Unknown

Contact Documentation Form

Student Name: _____   Class: _____

Date and Time: _____   Person Initiating: _____

Person Contacted	□ Parent/Guardian:	
	□ Counselor:	
	□ Nurse:	
	□ Administrator:	
	□ Other:	

Type of Contact	□ Phone Call/Text	□ Email
	□ Informal Meeting	□ Letter/Note
	□ Arranged Meeting	□ Class Dojo
	□ Other: _____	

Phone Call Response	□ No Answer	□ Wrong Number _____	□ Left Voicemail	□ Sent Text

Topic Discussed	□ Grades	□ Behavior
	□ Homework	□ Class work
	□ Projects	□ Schedule Meeting
Notes/Other:		

Action to be Taken:

Contact Purpose	□ Glow	□ Grow

Be a Pineapple. Stand tall. Wear a Crown, and Be sweet on the inside. - Unknown

Contact Documentation Form

Student Name: _____   Class: _____

Date and Time: _____   Person Initiating: _____

Person Contacted	□ Parent/Guardian:
	□ Counselor:
	□ Nurse:
	□ Administrator:
	□ Other:

Type of Contact	□ Phone Call/Text	□ Email
	□ Informal Meeting	□ Letter/Note
	□ Arranged Meeting	□ Class Dojo
	□ Other: _____	

Phone Call Response	□ No Answer	□ Wrong Number _____	□ Left Voicemail	□ Sent Text

Topic Discussed	□ Grades	□ Behavior
	□ Homework	□ Class work
	□ Projects	□ Schedule Meeting
Notes/Other:		

Action to be Taken:

Contact Purpose	□ Glow	□ Grow

The first step to getting somewhere is to decide you're not going to stay where you are. – J.P. Morgan

Contact Documentation Form

Student Name: _____ Class: _____

Date and Time: _____ Person Initiating: _____

Person Contacted	☐ Parent/Guardian:
	☐ Counselor:
	☐ Nurse:
	☐ Administrator:
	☐ Other:

Type of Contact	☐ Phone Call/Text	☐ Email
	☐ Informal Meeting	☐ Letter/Note
	☐ Arranged Meeting	☐ Class Dojo
	☐ Other: _____	

Phone Call Response	☐ No Answer	☐ Wrong Number _____	☐ Left Voicemail	☐ Sent Text

Topic Discussed	☐ Grades	☐ Behavior
	☐ Homework	☐ Class work
	☐ Projects	☐ Schedule Meeting
Notes/Other:		

Action to be Taken:

Contact Purpose	☐ Glow	☐ Grow

Believe in yourself a little more.

Contact Documentation Form

Student Name: _____   Class: _____

Date and Time: _____   Person Initiating: _____

Person Contacted	☐ Parent/Guardian:
	☐ Counselor:
	☐ Nurse:
	☐ Administrator:
	☐ Other:

Type of Contact	☐ Phone Call/Text	☐ Email
	☐ Informal Meeting	☐ Letter/Note
	☐ Arranged Meeting	☐ Class Dojo
	☐ Other: _____	

Phone Call Response	☐ No Answer	☐ Wrong Number _____	☐ Left Voicemail	☐ Sent Text

Topic Discussed	☐ Grades	☐ Behavior
	☐ Homework	☐ Class work
	☐ Projects	☐ Schedule Meeting
Notes/Other:		

Action to be Taken:

Contact Purpose	☐ Glow	☐ Grow

There is only one corner of the universe you can be certain improving and that's your own self.

-Aldous Huxley

Contact Documentation Form

Student Name: _____   Class: _____

Date and Time: _____   Person Initiating: _____

Person Contacted	☐ Parent/Guardian:
	☐ Counselor:
	☐ Nurse:
	☐ Administrator:
	☐ Other:

Type of Contact	☐ Phone Call/Text	☐ Email
	☐ Informal Meeting	☐ Letter/Note
	☐ Arranged Meeting	☐ Class Dojo
	☐ Other: _____	

Phone Call Response	☐ No Answer	☐ Wrong Number _____	☐ Left Voicemail	☐ Sent Text

Topic Discussed	☐ Grades	☐ Behavior
	☐ Homework	☐ Class work
	☐ Projects	☐ Schedule Meeting
Notes/Other:		

Action to be Taken:

Contact Purpose	☐ Glow	☐ Grow

A thousand mistakes are an education if you learn something from every one of them.

Contact Documentation Form

Student Name: _____   Class: _____

Date and Time: _____   Person Initiating: _____

Person Contacted	☐ Parent/Guardian:
	☐ Counselor:
	☐ Nurse:
	☐ Administrator:
	☐ Other:

Type of Contact	☐ Phone Call/Text	☐ Email
	☐ Informal Meeting	☐ Letter/Note
	☐ Arranged Meeting	☐ Class Dojo
	☐ Other: _____	

Phone Call Response	☐ No Answer	☐ Wrong Number _____	☐ Left Voicemail	☐ Sent Text

Topic Discussed	☐ Grades	☐ Behavior
	☐ Homework	☐ Class work
	☐ Projects	☐ Schedule Meeting
Notes/Other:		

Action to be Taken:

Contact Purpose	☐ Glow	☐ Grow

I can. I will. End of story.

Contact Documentation Form

Student Name: _____ Class: _____

Date and Time: _____ Person Initiating: _____

Person Contacted	☐ Parent/Guardian:
	☐ Counselor:
	☐ Nurse:
	☐ Administrator:
	☐ Other:

Type of Contact	☐ Phone Call/Text	☐ Email
	☐ Informal Meeting	☐ Letter/Note
	☐ Arranged Meeting	☐ Class Dojo
	☐ Other: _____	

Phone Call Response	☐ No Answer	☐ Wrong Number _____	☐ Left Voicemail	☐ Sent Text

Topic Discussed	☐ Grades	☐ Behavior
	☐ Homework	☐ Class work
	☐ Projects	☐ Schedule Meeting

Notes/Other:

Action to be Taken:

Contact Purpose	☐ Glow	☐ Grow

You are capable of amazing things.

Contact Documentation Form

Student Name: _____   Class: _____

Date and Time: _____   Person Initiating: _____

Person Contacted	☐ Parent/Guardian:
	☐ Counselor:
	☐ Nurse:
	☐ Administrator:
	☐ Other:

Type of Contact	☐ Phone Call/Text	☐ Email
	☐ Informal Meeting	☐ Letter/Note
	☐ Arranged Meeting	☐ Class Dojo
	☐ Other: _____	

Phone Call Response	☐ No Answer	☐ Wrong Number _____	☐ Left Voicemail	☐ Sent Text

Topic Discussed	☐ Grades	☐ Behavior
	☐ Homework	☐ Class work
	☐ Projects	☐ Schedule Meeting
Notes/Other:		

Action to be Taken:

Contact Purpose	☐ Glow	☐ Grow

Be careful how you are talking to yourself because you are listening.

Contact Documentation Form

Student Name: _____   Class: _____

Date and Time: _____   Person Initiating: _____

Person Contacted	□ Parent/Guardian:	
	□ Counselor:	
	□ Nurse:	
	□ Administrator:	
	□ Other:	

Type of Contact	□ Phone Call/Text	□ Email
	□ Informal Meeting	□ Letter/Note
	□ Arranged Meeting	□ Class Dojo
	□ Other: _____	

Phone Call Response	□ No Answer	□ Wrong Number _____	□ Left Voicemail	□ Sent Text

Topic Discussed	□ Grades	□ Behavior
	□ Homework	□ Class work
	□ Projects	□ Schedule Meeting
Notes/Other:		

Action to be Taken:

Contact Purpose	□ Glow	□ Grow

I'm too busy working on my own grass to notice if yours is greener.

Contact Documentation Form

Student Name: _____   Class: _____

Date and Time: _____   Person Initiating: _____

Person Contacted	☐ Parent/Guardian:
	☐ Counselor:
	☐ Nurse:
	☐ Administrator:
	☐ Other:

Type of Contact	☐ Phone Call/Text	☐ Email
	☐ Informal Meeting	☐ Letter/Note
	☐ Arranged Meeting	☐ Class Dojo
	☐ Other: _____	

Phone Call Response	☐ No Answer	☐ Wrong Number _____	☐ Left Voicemail	☐ Sent Text

Topic Discussed	☐ Grades	☐ Behavior
	☐ Homework	☐ Class work
	☐ Projects	☐ Schedule Meeting

Notes/Other:

Action to be Taken:

Contact Purpose	☐ Glow	☐ Grow

You can totally do this!!

Contact Documentation Form

Student Name: _____   Class: _____

Date and Time: _____   Person Initiating: _____

Person Contacted	☐ Parent/Guardian:
	☐ Counselor:
	☐ Nurse:
	☐ Administrator:
	☐ Other:

Type of Contact	☐ Phone Call/Text	☐ Email
	☐ Informal Meeting	☐ Letter/Note
	☐ Arranged Meeting	☐ Class Dojo
	☐ Other: _____	

Phone Call Response	☐ No Answer	☐ Wrong Number _____	☐ Left Voicemail	☐ Sent Text

Topic Discussed	☐ Grades	☐ Behavior
	☐ Homework	☐ Class work
	☐ Projects	☐ Schedule Meeting
Notes/Other:		

Action to be Taken:

Contact Purpose	☐ Glow	☐ Grow

No pressure. No diamonds.

Contact Documentation Form

Student Name: _____   Class: _____

Date and Time: _____   Person Initiating: _____

Person Contacted	☐ Parent/Guardian:
	☐ Counselor:
	☐ Nurse:
	☐ Administrator:
	☐ Other:

Type of Contact	☐ Phone Call/Text	☐ Email
	☐ Informal Meeting	☐ Letter/Note
	☐ Arranged Meeting	☐ Class Dojo
	☐ Other: _____	

Phone Call Response	☐ No Answer	☐ Wrong Number _____	☐ Left Voicemail	☐ Sent Text

Topic Discussed	☐ Grades	☐ Behavior
	☐ Homework	☐ Class work
	☐ Projects	☐ Schedule Meeting
Notes/Other:		

Action to be Taken:

Contact Purpose	☐ Glow	☐ Grow

Life is better when you're laughing...

72

Contact Documentation Form

Student Name: _____   Class: _____

Date and Time: _____   Person Initiating: _____

Person Contacted	☐ Parent/Guardian:
	☐ Counselor:
	☐ Nurse:
	☐ Administrator:
	☐ Other:

Type of Contact	☐ Phone Call/Text	☐ Email
	☐ Informal Meeting	☐ Letter/Note
	☐ Arranged Meeting	☐ Class Dojo
	☐ Other: _____	

Phone Call Response	☐ No Answer	☐ Wrong Number _____	☐ Left Voicemail	☐ Sent Text

Topic Discussed	☐ Grades	☐ Behavior
	☐ Homework	☐ Class work
	☐ Projects	☐ Schedule Meeting
Notes/Other:		

Action to be Taken:

Contact Purpose	☐ Glow	☐ Grow

If you want to fly, give up everything that weighs you down. - Budhha

73

Contact Documentation Form

Student Name: _____   Class: _____

Date and Time: _____   Person Initiating: _____

Person Contacted	
	☐ Parent/Guardian:
	☐ Counselor:
	☐ Nurse:
	☐ Administrator:
	☐ Other:

Type of Contact		
	☐ Phone Call/Text	☐ Email
	☐ Informal Meeting	☐ Letter/Note
	☐ Arranged Meeting	☐ Class Dojo
	☐ Other: _____	

Phone Call Response	☐ No Answer	☐ Wrong Number _____	☐ Left Voicemail	☐ Sent Text

Topic Discussed		
	☐ Grades	☐ Behavior
	☐ Homework	☐ Class work
	☐ Projects	☐ Schedule Meeting
Notes/Other:		

Action to be Taken:

Contact Purpose	☐ Glow	☐ Grow

A smart person knows what to say; a wise person knows whether or not to say it.

74

Contact Documentation Form

Student Name: _____   Class: _____

Date and Time: _____   Person Initiating: _____

Person Contacted	□ Parent/Guardian:
	□ Counselor:
	□ Nurse:
	□ Administrator:
	□ Other:

Type of Contact	□ Phone Call/Text	□ Email
	□ Informal Meeting	□ Letter/Note
	□ Arranged Meeting	□ Class Dojo
	□ Other: _____	

Phone Call Response	□ No Answer	□ Wrong Number _____	□ Left Voicemail	□ Sent Text

Topic Discussed	□ Grades	□ Behavior
	□ Homework	□ Class work
	□ Projects	□ Schedule Meeting
Notes/Other:		

Action to be Taken:

Contact Purpose	□ Glow	□ Grow

Count your blessings. Name them one by one and see what the Lord has done.

Contact Documentation Form

Student Name: _____   Class: _____

Date and Time: _____   Person Initiating: _____

Person Contacted	☐ Parent/Guardian:
	☐ Counselor:
	☐ Nurse:
	☐ Administrator:
	☐ Other:

Type of Contact	☐ Phone Call/Text	☐ Email
	☐ Informal Meeting	☐ Letter/Note
	☐ Arranged Meeting	☐ Class Dojo
	☐ Other: _____	

Phone Call Response	☐ No Answer	☐ Wrong Number _____	☐ Left Voicemail	☐ Sent Text

Topic Discussed	☐ Grades	☐ Behavior
	☐ Homework	☐ Class work
	☐ Projects	☐ Schedule Meeting

Notes/Other:

Action to be Taken:

Contact Purpose	☐ Glow	☐ Grow

No rain. No flowers.

Contact Documentation Form

Student Name: _____   Class: _____

Date and Time: _____   Person Initiating: _____

Person Contacted	□ Parent/Guardian:
	□ Counselor:
	□ Nurse:
	□ Administrator:
	□ Other:

Type of Contact	□ Phone Call/Text	□ Email
	□ Informal Meeting	□ Letter/Note
	□ Arranged Meeting	□ Class Dojo
	□ Other: _____	

Phone Call Response	□ No Answer	□ Wrong Number _____	□ Left Voicemail	□ Sent Text

Topic Discussed	□ Grades	□ Behavior
	□ Homework	□ Class work
	□ Projects	□ Schedule Meeting
Notes/Other:		

Action to be Taken:

Contact Purpose	□ Glow	□ Grow

NEVER DULL YOUR SUNSHINE FOR SOMEONE ELSE.

Contact Documentation Form

Student Name: _____ Class: _____

Date and Time: _____ Person Initiating: _____

Person Contacted	□ Parent/Guardian:
	□ Counselor:
	□ Nurse:
	□ Administrator:
	□ Other:

Type of Contact	□ Phone Call/Text	□ Email
	□ Informal Meeting	□ Letter/Note
	□ Arranged Meeting	□ Class Dojo
	□ Other: _____	

Phone Call Response	□ No Answer	□ Wrong Number _____	□ Left Voicemail	□ Sent Text

Topic Discussed	□ Grades	□ Behavior
	□ Homework	□ Class work
	□ Projects	□ Schedule Meeting
Notes/Other:		

Action to be Taken:

Contact Purpose	□ Glow	□ Grow

Life is too short to wait until tomorrow.

Contact Documentation Form

Student Name: _____   Class: _____

Date and Time: _____   Person Initiating: _____

Person Contacted	☐ Parent/Guardian:	
	☐ Counselor:	
	☐ Nurse:	
	☐ Administrator:	
	☐ Other:	

Type of Contact	☐ Phone Call/Text	☐ Email
	☐ Informal Meeting	☐ Letter/Note
	☐ Arranged Meeting	☐ Class Dojo
	☐ Other: _____	

Phone Call Response	☐ No Answer	☐ Wrong Number _____	☐ Left Voicemail	☐ Sent Text

Topic Discussed	☐ Grades	☐ Behavior
	☐ Homework	☐ Class work
	☐ Projects	☐ Schedule Meeting

Notes/Other:

Action to be Taken:

Contact Purpose	☐ Glow	☐ Grow

Life is a onetime offer. Use it well.

Contact Documentation Form

Student Name: _____   Class: _____

Date and Time: _____   Person Initiating: _____

Person Contacted	☐ Parent/Guardian:
	☐ Counselor:
	☐ Nurse:
	☐ Administrator:
	☐ Other:

Type of Contact	☐ Phone Call/Text	☐ Email
	☐ Informal Meeting	☐ Letter/Note
	☐ Arranged Meeting	☐ Class Dojo
	☐ Other: _____	

Phone Call Response	☐ No Answer	☐ Wrong Number _____	☐ Left Voicemail	☐ Sent Text

Topic Discussed	☐ Grades	☐ Behavior
	☐ Homework	☐ Class work
	☐ Projects	☐ Schedule Meeting
Notes/Other:		

Action to be Taken:

Contact Purpose	☐ Glow	☐ Grow

Nothing changes if nothing changes.

Contact Documentation Form

Student Name: _____   Class: _____

Date and Time: _____   Person Initiating: _____

Person Contacted	☐ Parent/Guardian:
	☐ Counselor:
	☐ Nurse:
	☐ Administrator:
	☐ Other:

Type of Contact	☐ Phone Call/Text	☐ Email
	☐ Informal Meeting	☐ Letter/Note
	☐ Arranged Meeting	☐ Class Dojo
	☐ Other: _____	

Phone Call Response	☐ No Answer	☐ Wrong Number _____	☐ Left Voicemail	☐ Sent Text

Topic Discussed	☐ Grades	☐ Behavior
	☐ Homework	☐ Class work
	☐ Projects	☐ Schedule Meeting
Notes/Other:		

Action to be Taken:

Contact Purpose	☐ Glow	☐ Grow

Sometimes you have to keep good news to yourself. Everybody is not genuinely happy for you.

Contact Documentation Form

Student Name: _____   Class: _____

Date and Time: _____   Person Initiating: _____

Person Contacted	□ Parent/Guardian:	
	□ Counselor:	
	□ Nurse:	
	□ Administrator:	
	□ Other:	

Type of Contact	□ Phone Call/Text	□ Email
	□ Informal Meeting	□ Letter/Note
	□ Arranged Meeting	□ Class Dojo
	□ Other: _____	

Phone Call Response	□ No Answer	□ Wrong Number _____	□ Left Voicemail	□ Sent Text

Topic Discussed	□ Grades	□ Behavior
	□ Homework	□ Class work
	□ Projects	□ Schedule Meeting
Notes/Other:		

Action to be Taken:

Contact Purpose	□ Glow	□ Grow

If someone doesn't appreciate your presence, make them appreciate your absence.

Contact Documentation Form

Student Name: _____   Class: _____

Date and Time: _____   Person Initiating: _____

Person Contacted	☐ Parent/Guardian:
	☐ Counselor:
	☐ Nurse:
	☐ Administrator:
	☐ Other:

Type of Contact	☐ Phone Call/Text	☐ Email
	☐ Informal Meeting	☐ Letter/Note
	☐ Arranged Meeting	☐ Class Dojo
	☐ Other: _____	

Phone Call Response	☐ No Answer	☐ Wrong Number _____	☐ Left Voicemail	☐ Sent Text

Topic Discussed	☐ Grades	☐ Behavior
	☐ Homework	☐ Class work
	☐ Projects	☐ Schedule Meeting
Notes/Other:		

Action to be Taken:

Contact Purpose	☐ Glow	☐ Grow

Do more of what makes you happy.

Contact Documentation Form

Student Name: _____ Class: _____

Date and Time: _____ Person Initiating: _____

Person Contacted	□ Parent/Guardian:
	□ Counselor:
	□ Nurse:
	□ Administrator:
	□ Other:

Type of Contact	□ Phone Call/Text	□ Email
	□ Informal Meeting	□ Letter/Note
	□ Arranged Meeting	□ Class Dojo
	□ Other: _____	

Phone Call Response	□ No Answer	□ Wrong Number _____	□ Left Voicemail	□ Sent Text

Topic Discussed	□ Grades	□ Behavior
	□ Homework	□ Class work
	□ Projects	□ Schedule Meeting
Notes/Other:		

Action to be Taken:

Contact Purpose	□ Glow	□ Grow

Every master was once a beginner.

Contact Documentation Form

Student Name: _____   Class: _____

Date and Time: _____   Person Initiating: _____

Person Contacted	
	☐ Parent/Guardian:
	☐ Counselor:
	☐ Nurse:
	☐ Administrator:
	☐ Other:

Type of Contact		
	☐ Phone Call/Text	☐ Email
	☐ Informal Meeting	☐ Letter/Note
	☐ Arranged Meeting	☐ Class Dojo
	☐ Other: _____	

Phone Call Response	☐ No Answer	☐ Wrong Number _____	☐ Left Voicemail	☐ Sent Text

Topic Discussed		
	☐ Grades	☐ Behavior
	☐ Homework	☐ Class work
	☐ Projects	☐ Schedule Meeting
Notes/Other:		

Action to be Taken:

Contact Purpose	☐ Glow	☐ Grow

Don't hold on to thoughts that don't allow your mind to move forward.

Contact Documentation Form

Student Name: _____   Class: _____

Date and Time: _____   Person Initiating: _____

Person Contacted	☐ Parent/Guardian:
	☐ Counselor:
	☐ Nurse:
	☐ Administrator:
	☐ Other:

Type of Contact	☐ Phone Call/Text	☐ Email
	☐ Informal Meeting	☐ Letter/Note
	☐ Arranged Meeting	☐ Class Dojo
	☐ Other: _____	

Phone Call Response	☐ No Answer	☐ Wrong Number _____	☐ Left Voicemail	☐ Sent Text

Topic Discussed	☐ Grades	☐ Behavior
	☐ Homework	☐ Class work
	☐ Projects	☐ Schedule Meeting
Notes/Other:		

Action to be Taken:

Contact Purpose	☐ Glow	☐ Grow

NOTE TO SELF: STOP TRYING SO HARD FOR PEOPLE WHO DON'T CARE.

Contact Documentation Form

Student Name: _____ Class: _____

Date and Time: _____ Person Initiating: _____

Person Contacted	☐ Parent/Guardian:
	☐ Counselor:
	☐ Nurse:
	☐ Administrator:
	☐ Other:

Type of Contact	☐ Phone Call/Text	☐ Email
	☐ Informal Meeting	☐ Letter/Note
	☐ Arranged Meeting	☐ Class Dojo
	☐ Other: _____	

Phone Call Response	☐ No Answer	☐ Wrong Number _____	☐ Left Voicemail	☐ Sent Text

Topic Discussed	☐ Grades	☐ Behavior
	☐ Homework	☐ Class work
	☐ Projects	☐ Schedule Meeting
Notes/Other:		

Action to be Taken:

Contact Purpose	☐ Glow	☐ Grow

Many a false step is made by standing still.

Contact Documentation Form

Student Name: _____   Class: _____

Date and Time: _____   Person Initiating: _____

Person Contacted	□ Parent/Guardian:
	□ Counselor:
	□ Nurse:
	□ Administrator:
	□ Other:

Type of Contact	□ Phone Call/Text	□ Email
	□ Informal Meeting	□ Letter/Note
	□ Arranged Meeting	□ Class Dojo
	□ Other: _____	

Phone Call Response	□ No Answer	□ Wrong Number _____	□ Left Voicemail	□ Sent Text

Topic Discussed	□ Grades	□ Behavior
	□ Homework	□ Class work
	□ Projects	□ Schedule Meeting
Notes/Other:		

Action to be Taken:

Contact Purpose	□ Glow	□ Grow

Know God, Know Peace.

Contact Documentation Form

Student Name: _____   Class: _____

Date and Time: _____   Person Initiating: _____

Person Contacted	□ Parent/Guardian:
	□ Counselor:
	□ Nurse:
	□ Administrator:
	□ Other:

Type of Contact	□ Phone Call/Text	□ Email
	□ Informal Meeting	□ Letter/Note
	□ Arranged Meeting	□ Class Dojo
	□ Other: _____	

Phone Call Response	□ No Answer	□ Wrong Number _____	□ Left Voicemail	□ Sent Text

Topic Discussed	□ Grades	□ Behavior
	□ Homework	□ Class work
	□ Projects	□ Schedule Meeting
Notes/Other:		

Action to be Taken:

Contact Purpose	□ Glow	□ Grow

Accept everything you are and nothing you are not.

Contact Documentation Form

Student Name: _____   Class: _____

Date and Time: _____   Person Initiating: _____

Person Contacted	☐ Parent/Guardian:
	☐ Counselor:
	☐ Nurse:
	☐ Administrator:
	☐ Other:

Type of Contact	☐ Phone Call/Text	☐ Email
	☐ Informal Meeting	☐ Letter/Note
	☐ Arranged Meeting	☐ Class Dojo
	☐ Other: _____	

Phone Call Response	☐ No Answer	☐ Wrong Number _____	☐ Left Voicemail	☐ Sent Text

Topic Discussed	☐ Grades	☐ Behavior
	☐ Homework	☐ Class work
	☐ Projects	☐ Schedule Meeting
Notes/Other:		

Action to be Taken:

Contact Purpose	☐ Glow	☐ Grow

This will make perfect sense one day.

Contact Documentation Form

Student Name: _____ Class: _____

Date and Time: _____ Person Initiating: _____

Person Contacted	☐ Parent/Guardian:
	☐ Counselor:
	☐ Nurse:
	☐ Administrator:
	☐ Other:

Type of Contact	☐ Phone Call/Text	☐ Email
	☐ Informal Meeting	☐ Letter/Note
	☐ Arranged Meeting	☐ Class Dojo
	☐ Other: _____	

Phone Call Response	☐ No Answer	☐ Wrong Number _____	☐ Left Voicemail	☐ Sent Text

Topic Discussed	☐ Grades	☐ Behavior
	☐ Homework	☐ Class work
	☐ Projects	☐ Schedule Meeting
Notes/Other:		

Action to be Taken:

Contact Purpose	☐ Glow	☐ Grow

Remember to live.

Contact Documentation Form

Student Name: _____   Class: _____

Date and Time: _____   Person Initiating: _____

Person Contacted	□ Parent/Guardian:
	□ Counselor:
	□ Nurse:
	□ Administrator:
	□ Other:

Type of Contact	□ Phone Call/Text	□ Email
	□ Informal Meeting	□ Letter/Note
	□ Arranged Meeting	□ Class Dojo
	□ Other: _____	

Phone Call Response	□ No Answer	□ Wrong Number _____	□ Left Voicemail	□ Sent Text

Topic Discussed	□ Grades	□ Behavior
	□ Homework	□ Class work
	□ Projects	□ Schedule Meeting
Notes/Other:		

Action to be Taken:

Contact Purpose	□ Glow	□ Grow

It's okay if the only thing you did today was breathe.

Contact Documentation Form

Student Name: _____   Class: _____

Date and Time: _____   Person Initiating: _____

Person Contacted	□ Parent/Guardian:
	□ Counselor:
	□ Nurse:
	□ Administrator:
	□ Other:

Type of Contact	□ Phone Call/Text	□ Email
	□ Informal Meeting	□ Letter/Note
	□ Arranged Meeting	□ Class Dojo
	□ Other: _____	

Phone Call Response	□ No Answer	□ Wrong Number _____	□ Left Voicemail	□ Sent Text

Topic Discussed	□ Grades	□ Behavior
	□ Homework	□ Class work
	□ Projects	□ Schedule Meeting
Notes/Other:		

Action to be Taken:

Contact Purpose	□ Glow	□ Grow

Be selective in your battles. Sometimes peace is better than being right.

Contact Documentation Form

Student Name: _____   Class: _____

Date and Time: _____   Person Initiating: _____

Person Contacted	☐ Parent/Guardian:
	☐ Counselor:
	☐ Nurse:
	☐ Administrator:
	☐ Other:

Type of Contact	☐ Phone Call/Text	☐ Email
	☐ Informal Meeting	☐ Letter/Note
	☐ Arranged Meeting	☐ Class Dojo
	☐ Other: _____	

Phone Call Response	☐ No Answer	☐ Wrong Number _____	☐ Left Voicemail	☐ Sent Text

Topic Discussed	☐ Grades	☐ Behavior
	☐ Homework	☐ Class work
	☐ Projects	☐ Schedule Meeting
Notes/Other:		

Action to be Taken:

Contact Purpose	☐ Glow	☐ Grow

Why follow when you can LEAD.

94

Contact Documentation Form

Student Name: _____ Class: _____

Date and Time: _____ Person Initiating: _____

Person Contacted	□ Parent/Guardian:
	□ Counselor:
	□ Nurse:
	□ Administrator:
	□ Other:

Type of Contact	□ Phone Call/Text	□ Email
	□ Informal Meeting	□ Letter/Note
	□ Arranged Meeting	□ Class Dojo
	□ Other: _____	

Phone Call Response	□ No Answer	□ Wrong Number _____	□ Left Voicemail	□ Sent Text

Topic Discussed	□ Grades	□ Behavior
	□ Homework	□ Class work
	□ Projects	□ Schedule Meeting
Notes/Other:		

Action to be Taken:

Contact Purpose	□ Glow	□ Grow

Carpe Diem.

Contact Documentation Form

Student Name: _____   Class: _____

Date and Time: _____   Person Initiating: _____

Person Contacted	□ Parent/Guardian:
	□ Counselor:
	□ Nurse:
	□ Administrator:
	□ Other:

Type of Contact	□ Phone Call/Text	□ Email
	□ Informal Meeting	□ Letter/Note
	□ Arranged Meeting	□ Class Dojo
	□ Other: _____	

Phone Call Response	□ No Answer	□ Wrong Number _____	□ Left Voicemail	□ Sent Text

Topic Discussed	□ Grades	□ Behavior
	□ Homework	□ Class work
	□ Projects	□ Schedule Meeting
Notes/Other:		

Action to be Taken:

Contact Purpose	□ Glow	□ Grow

Still I rise.

Contact Documentation Form

Student Name: _____   Class: _____

Date and Time: _____   Person Initiating: _____

Person Contacted	☐ Parent/Guardian:
	☐ Counselor:
	☐ Nurse:
	☐ Administrator:
	☐ Other:

Type of Contact	☐ Phone Call/Text	☐ Email
	☐ Informal Meeting	☐ Letter/Note
	☐ Arranged Meeting	☐ Class Dojo
	☐ Other: _____	

Phone Call Response	☐ No Answer	☐ Wrong Number _____	☐ Left Voicemail	☐ Sent Text

Topic Discussed	☐ Grades	☐ Behavior
	☐ Homework	☐ Class work
	☐ Projects	☐ Schedule Meeting
Notes/Other:		

Action to be Taken:

Contact Purpose	☐ Glow	☐ Grow

Coffee and kindness…maybe two coffees and then kindness.

Contact Documentation Form

Student Name: _____   Class: _____

Date and Time: _____   Person Initiating: _____

Person Contacted	□ Parent/Guardian:
	□ Counselor:
	□ Nurse:
	□ Administrator:
	□ Other:

Type of Contact	□ Phone Call/Text	□ Email
	□ Informal Meeting	□ Letter/Note
	□ Arranged Meeting	□ Class Dojo
	□ Other: _____	

Phone Call Response	□ No Answer	□ Wrong Number _____	□ Left Voicemail	□ Sent Text

Topic Discussed	□ Grades	□ Behavior
	□ Homework	□ Class work
	□ Projects	□ Schedule Meeting
Notes/Other:		

Action to be Taken:

Contact Purpose	□ Glow	□ Grow

THE DREAM IS FREE. THE HUSTLE IS SOLD SEPARATELY.

Contact Documentation Form

Student Name: _____ Class: _____

Date and Time: _____ Person Initiating: _____

Person Contacted	□ Parent/Guardian:
	□ Counselor:
	□ Nurse:
	□ Administrator:
	□ Other:

Type of Contact	□ Phone Call/Text	□ Email
	□ Informal Meeting	□ Letter/Note
	□ Arranged Meeting	□ Class Dojo
	□ Other: _____	

Phone Call Response	□ No Answer	□ Wrong Number _____	□ Left Voicemail	□ Sent Text

Topic Discussed	□ Grades	□ Behavior
	□ Homework	□ Class work
	□ Projects	□ Schedule Meeting
Notes/Other:		

Action to be Taken:

Contact Purpose	□ Glow	□ Grow

Stay strong. Your story isn't over yet.

Contact Documentation Form

Student Name: _____   Class: _____

Date and Time: _____   Person Initiating: _____

Person Contacted	☐ Parent/Guardian:	
	☐ Counselor:	
	☐ Nurse:	
	☐ Administrator:	
	☐ Other:	

Type of Contact	☐ Phone Call/Text	☐ Email
	☐ Informal Meeting	☐ Letter/Note
	☐ Arranged Meeting	☐ Class Dojo
	☐ Other: _____	

Phone Call Response	☐ No Answer	☐ Wrong Number _____	☐ Left Voicemail	☐ Sent Text

Topic Discussed	☐ Grades	☐ Behavior
	☐ Homework	☐ Class work
	☐ Projects	☐ Schedule Meeting
Notes/Other:		

Action to be Taken:

Contact Purpose	☐ Glow	☐ Grow

Smile and walk away.

Contact Documentation Form

Student Name: _____   Class: _____

Date and Time: _____   Person Initiating: _____

Person Contacted	☐ Parent/Guardian:
	☐ Counselor:
	☐ Nurse:
	☐ Administrator:
	☐ Other:

Type of Contact	☐ Phone Call/Text	☐ Email
	☐ Informal Meeting	☐ Letter/Note
	☐ Arranged Meeting	☐ Class Dojo
	☐ Other: _____	

Phone Call Response	☐ No Answer	☐ Wrong Number _____	☐ Left Voicemail	☐ Sent Text

Topic Discussed	☐ Grades	☐ Behavior
	☐ Homework	☐ Class work
	☐ Projects	☐ Schedule Meeting
Notes/Other:		

Action to be Taken:

Contact Purpose	☐ Glow	☐ Grow

Let gratitude be your attitude.

Contact Documentation Form

Student Name: _____   Class: _____

Date and Time: _____   Person Initiating: _____

Person Contacted	☐ Parent/Guardian:
	☐ Counselor:
	☐ Nurse:
	☐ Administrator:
	☐ Other:

Type of Contact	☐ Phone Call/Text	☐ Email
	☐ Informal Meeting	☐ Letter/Note
	☐ Arranged Meeting	☐ Class Dojo
	☐ Other: _____	

Phone Call Response	☐ No Answer	☐ Wrong Number _____	☐ Left Voicemail	☐ Sent Text

Topic Discussed	☐ Grades	☐ Behavior
	☐ Homework	☐ Class work
	☐ Projects	☐ Schedule Meeting
Notes/Other:		

Action to be Taken:

Contact Purpose	☐ Glow	☐ Grow

If you want the rainbow, you have to deal with the rain.

Contact Documentation Form

Student Name: _____   Class: _____

Date and Time: _____   Person Initiating: _____

Person Contacted	☐ Parent/Guardian:
	☐ Counselor:
	☐ Nurse:
	☐ Administrator:
	☐ Other:

Type of Contact	☐ Phone Call/Text	☐ Email
	☐ Informal Meeting	☐ Letter/Note
	☐ Arranged Meeting	☐ Class Dojo
	☐ Other: _____	

Phone Call Response	☐ No Answer	☐ Wrong Number _____	☐ Left Voicemail	☐ Sent Text

Topic Discussed	☐ Grades	☐ Behavior
	☐ Homework	☐ Class work
	☐ Projects	☐ Schedule Meeting
Notes/Other:		

Action to be Taken:

Contact Purpose	☐ Glow	☐ Grow

But God!

School Year

Contact Documentation Form

Student Name: _____   Class: _____

Date and Time: _____   Person Initiating: _____

Person Contacted	☐ Parent/Guardian:
	☐ Counselor:
	☐ Nurse:
	☐ Administrator:
	☐ Other:

Type of Contact	☐ Phone Call/Text	☐ Email
	☐ Informal Meeting	☐ Letter/Note
	☐ Arranged Meeting	☐ Class Dojo
	☐ Other: _____	

Phone Call Response	☐ No Answer	☐ Wrong Number _____	☐ Left Voicemail	☐ Sent Text

Topic Discussed	☐ Grades	☐ Behavior
	☐ Homework	☐ Class work
	☐ Projects	☐ Schedule Meeting
Notes/Other:		

Action to be Taken:

Contact Purpose	☐ Glow	☐ Grow

Life has 2 rules. #1-Never Quit #2-Always remember rule #1 – Unknown

Contact Documentation Form

Student Name: _____ Class: _____

Date and Time: _____ Person Initiating: _____

Person Contacted	□ Parent/Guardian:
	□ Counselor:
	□ Nurse:
	□ Administrator:
	□ Other:

Type of Contact	□ Phone Call/Text	□ Email
	□ Informal Meeting	□ Letter/Note
	□ Arranged Meeting	□ Class Dojo
	□ Other: _____	

Phone Call Response	□ No Answer	□ Wrong Number _____	□ Left Voicemail	□ Sent Text

Topic Discussed	□ Grades	□ Behavior
	□ Homework	□ Class work
	□ Projects	□ Schedule Meeting
Notes/Other:		

Action to be Taken:

Contact Purpose	□ Glow	□ Grow

Out of a mountain of despair, a stone of hope. – Martin Luther King, Jr.

Contact Documentation Form

Student Name: _____   Class: _____

Date and Time: _____   Person Initiating: _____

Person Contacted	☐ Parent/Guardian:
	☐ Counselor:
	☐ Nurse:
	☐ Administrator:
	☐ Other:

Type of Contact	☐ Phone Call/Text	☐ Email
	☐ Informal Meeting	☐ Letter/Note
	☐ Arranged Meeting	☐ Class Dojo
	☐ Other: _____	

Phone Call Response	☐ No Answer	☐ Wrong Number _____	☐ Left Voicemail	☐ Sent Text

Topic Discussed	☐ Grades	☐ Behavior
	☐ Homework	☐ Class work
	☐ Projects	☐ Schedule Meeting
Notes/Other:		

Action to be Taken:

Contact Purpose	☐ Glow	☐ Grow

Act as if what you do makes a difference. IT DOES. – *William James*

Contact Documentation Form

Student Name: _____   Class: _____

Date and Time: _____   Person Initiating: _____

Person Contacted	□ Parent/Guardian:
	□ Counselor:
	□ Nurse:
	□ Administrator:
	□ Other:

Type of Contact	□ Phone Call/Text	□ Email
	□ Informal Meeting	□ Letter/Note
	□ Arranged Meeting	□ Class Dojo
	□ Other: _____	

Phone Call Response	□ No Answer	□ Wrong Number _____	□ Left Voicemail	□ Sent Text

Topic Discussed	□ Grades	□ Behavior
	□ Homework	□ Class work
	□ Projects	□ Schedule Meeting
Notes/Other:		

Action to be Taken:

Contact Purpose	□ Glow	□ Grow

Nothing is impossible. The word itself says "I'm possible!" – *Audrey Hepburn*

Contact Documentation Form

Student Name: _____   Class: _____

Date and Time: _____   Person Initiating: _____

Person Contacted	□ Parent/Guardian:
	□ Counselor:
	□ Nurse:
	□ Administrator:
	□ Other:

Type of Contact	□ Phone Call/Text	□ Email
	□ Informal Meeting	□ Letter/Note
	□ Arranged Meeting	□ Class Dojo
	□ Other: _____	

Phone Call Response	□ No Answer	□ Wrong Number _____	□ Left Voicemail	□ Sent Text

Topic Discussed	□ Grades	□ Behavior
	□ Homework	□ Class work
	□ Projects	□ Schedule Meeting
Notes/Other:		

Action to be Taken:

Contact Purpose	□ Glow	□ Grow

Try to be a rainbow in someone else's cloud. — *Maya Angelou.*

Contact Documentation Form

Student Name: _____   Class: _____

Date and Time: _____   Person Initiating: _____

Person Contacted	☐ Parent/Guardian:
	☐ **Counselor:**
	☐ **Nurse:**
	☐ **Administrator:**
	☐ Other:

Type of Contact	☐ Phone Call/Text	☐ Email
	☐ Informal Meeting	☐ Letter/Note
	☐ Arranged Meeting	☐ Class Dojo
	☐ Other: _____	

Phone Call Response	☐ No Answer	☐ Wrong Number _____	☐ Left Voicemail	☐ Sent Text

Topic Discussed	☐ Grades	☐ Behavior
	☐ Homework	☐ Class work
	☐ Projects	☐ Schedule Meeting

Notes/Other:

Action to be Taken:

Contact Purpose	☐ Glow	☐ Grow

You are enough just as you are. — Megan Markle

Contact Documentation Form

Student Name: _____   Class: _____

Date and Time: _____   Person Initiating: _____

Person Contacted	☐ Parent/Guardian:	
	☐ Counselor:	
	☐ Nurse:	
	☐ Administrator:	
	☐ Other:	

Type of Contact	☐ Phone Call/Text	☐ Email
	☐ Informal Meeting	☐ Letter/Note
	☐ Arranged Meeting	☐ Class Dojo
	☐ Other: _____	

Phone Call Response	☐ No Answer	☐ Wrong Number _____	☐ Left Voicemail	☐ Sent Text

Topic Discussed	☐ Grades	☐ Behavior
	☐ Homework	☐ Class work
	☐ Projects	☐ Schedule Meeting
Notes/Other:		

Action to be Taken:

Contact Purpose	☐ Glow	☐ Grow

Leadership is about making others better as a result of your presence and making sure that impact lasts in your absence. - Unknown

Contact Documentation Form

Student Name: _____   Class: _____

Date and Time: _____   Person Initiating: _____

Person Contacted	☐ Parent/Guardian:
	☐ Counselor:
	☐ Nurse:
	☐ Administrator:
	☐ Other:

Type of Contact	☐ Phone Call/Text	☐ Email
	☐ Informal Meeting	☐ Letter/Note
	☐ Arranged Meeting	☐ Class Dojo
	☐ Other: _____	

Phone Call Response	☐ No Answer	☐ Wrong Number _____	☐ Left Voicemail	☐ Sent Text

Topic Discussed	☐ Grades	☐ Behavior
	☐ Homework	☐ Class work
	☐ Projects	☐ Schedule Meeting
Notes/Other:		

Action to be Taken:

Contact Purpose	☐ Glow	☐ Grow

Be a Pineapple. Stand tall. Wear a Crown. and Be sweet on the inside. - Unknown

Contact Documentation Form

Student Name: _____   Class: _____

Date and Time: _____   Person Initiating: _____

Person Contacted	☐ Parent/Guardian:
	☐ Counselor:
	☐ Nurse:
	☐ Administrator:
	☐ Other:

Type of Contact	☐ Phone Call/Text	☐ Email
	☐ Informal Meeting	☐ Letter/Note
	☐ Arranged Meeting	☐ Class Dojo
	☐ Other: _____	

Phone Call Response	☐ No Answer	☐ Wrong Number _____	☐ Left Voicemail	☐ Sent Text

Topic Discussed	☐ Grades	☐ Behavior
	☐ Homework	☐ Class work
	☐ Projects	☐ Schedule Meeting
Notes/Other:		

Action to be Taken:

Contact Purpose	☐ Glow	☐ Grow

The first step to getting somewhere is to decide you're not going to stay where you are. – J.P. Morgan

Contact Documentation Form

Student Name: _____   Class: _____

Date and Time: _____   Person Initiating: _____

Person Contacted	☐ Parent/Guardian:
	☐ Counselor:
	☐ Nurse:
	☐ Administrator:
	☐ Other:

Type of Contact	☐ Phone Call/Text	☐ Email
	☐ Informal Meeting	☐ Letter/Note
	☐ Arranged Meeting	☐ Class Dojo
	☐ Other: _____	

Phone Call Response	☐ No Answer	☐ Wrong Number _____	☐ Left Voicemail	☐ Sent Text

Topic Discussed	☐ Grades	☐ Behavior
	☐ Homework	☐ Class work
	☐ Projects	☐ Schedule Meeting
Notes/Other:		

Action to be Taken:

Contact Purpose	☐ Glow	☐ Grow

You can't go back and change the beginning but you can start where you are and change the ending. – C.S. Lewis

Contact Documentation Form

Student Name: _____   Class: _____

Date and Time: _____   Person Initiating: _____

Person Contacted	☐ Parent/Guardian:
	☐ Counselor:
	☐ Nurse:
	☐ Administrator:
	☐ Other:

Type of Contact	☐ Phone Call/Text	☐ Email
	☐ Informal Meeting	☐ Letter/Note
	☐ Arranged Meeting	☐ Class Dojo
	☐ Other: _____	

Phone Call Response	☐ No Answer	☐ Wrong Number _____	☐ Left Voicemail	☐ Sent Text

Topic Discussed	☐ Grades	☐ Behavior
	☐ Homework	☐ Class work
	☐ Projects	☐ Schedule Meeting
Notes/Other:		

Action to be Taken:

Contact Purpose	☐ Glow	☐ Grow

Believe in yourself a little more.

Contact Documentation Form

Student Name: _____   Class: _____

Date and Time: _____   Person Initiating: _____

Person Contacted	□ Parent/Guardian:
	□ Counselor:
	□ Nurse:
	□ Administrator:
	□ Other:

Type of Contact	□ Phone Call/Text	□ Email
	□ Informal Meeting	□ Letter/Note
	□ Arranged Meeting	□ Class Dojo
	□ Other: _____	

Phone Call Response	□ No Answer	□ Wrong Number _____	□ Left Voicemail	□ Sent Text

Topic Discussed	□ Grades	□ Behavior
	□ Homework	□ Class work
	□ Projects	□ Schedule Meeting
Notes/Other:		

Action to be Taken:

Contact Purpose	□ Glow	□ Grow

There is only one corner of the universe you can be certain improving and that's your own self.

-Aldous Huxley

Contact Documentation Form

Student Name: _____   Class: _____

Date and Time: _____   Person Initiating: _____

Person Contacted	☐ Parent/Guardian:
	☐ Counselor:
	☐ Nurse:
	☐ Administrator:
	☐ Other:

Type of Contact	☐ Phone Call/Text	☐ Email
	☐ Informal Meeting	☐ Letter/Note
	☐ Arranged Meeting	☐ Class Dojo
	☐ Other: _____	

Phone Call Response	☐ No Answer	☐ Wrong Number _____	☐ Left Voicemail	☐ Sent Text

Topic Discussed	☐ Grades	☐ Behavior
	☐ Homework	☐ Class work
	☐ Projects	☐ Schedule Meeting
Notes/Other:		

Action to be Taken:

Contact Purpose	☐ Glow	☐ Grow

A thousand mistakes are an education if you learn something from every one of them.

Contact Documentation Form

Student Name: _____   Class: _____

Date and Time: _____   Person Initiating: _____

Person Contacted	☐ Parent/Guardian:
	☐ Counselor:
	☐ Nurse:
	☐ Administrator:
	☐ Other:

Type of Contact	☐ Phone Call/Text	☐ Email
	☐ Informal Meeting	☐ Letter/Note
	☐ Arranged Meeting	☐ Class Dojo
	☐ Other: _____	

Phone Call Response	☐ No Answer	☐ Wrong Number _____	☐ Left Voicemail	☐ Sent Text

Topic Discussed	☐ Grades	☐ Behavior
	☐ Homework	☐ Class work
	☐ Projects	☐ Schedule Meeting
Notes/Other:		

Action to be Taken:

Contact Purpose	☐ Glow	☐ Grow

I can. I will. End of story.

Contact Documentation Form

Student Name: _____   Class: _____

Date and Time: _____   Person Initiating: _____

Person Contacted	□ Parent/Guardian:
	□ Counselor:
	□ Nurse:
	□ Administrator:
	□ Other:

Type of Contact	□ Phone Call/Text	□ Email
	□ Informal Meeting	□ Letter/Note
	□ Arranged Meeting	□ Class Dojo
	□ Other: _____	

Phone Call Response	□ No Answer	□ Wrong Number _____	□ Left Voicemail	□ Sent Text

Topic Discussed	□ Grades	□ Behavior
	□ Homework	□ Class work
	□ Projects	□ Schedule Meeting
Notes/Other:		

Action to be Taken:

Contact Purpose	□ Glow	□ Grow

You are capable of amazing things.

Contact Documentation Form

Student Name: _____ Class: _____

Date and Time: _____ Person Initiating: _____

Person Contacted	☐ Parent/Guardian:
	☐ Counselor:
	☐ Nurse:
	☐ Administrator:
	☐ Other:

Type of Contact	☐ Phone Call/Text	☐ Email
	☐ Informal Meeting	☐ Letter/Note
	☐ Arranged Meeting	☐ Class Dojo
	☐ Other: _____	

Phone Call Response	☐ No Answer	☐ Wrong Number _____	☐ Left Voicemail	☐ Sent Text

Topic Discussed	☐ Grades	☐ Behavior
	☐ Homework	☐ Class work
	☐ Projects	☐ Schedule Meeting
Notes/Other:		

Action to be Taken:

Contact Purpose	☐ Glow	☐ Grow

Be careful how you are talking to yourself because you are listening.

Contact Documentation Form

Student Name: _____   Class: _____

Date and Time: _____   Person Initiating: _____

Person Contacted	□ Parent/Guardian:
	□ Counselor:
	□ Nurse:
	□ Administrator:
	□ Other:

Type of Contact	□ Phone Call/Text	□ Email
	□ Informal Meeting	□ Letter/Note
	□ Arranged Meeting	□ Class Dojo
	□ Other: _____	

Phone Call Response	□ No Answer	□ Wrong Number _____	□ Left Voicemail	□ Sent Text

Topic Discussed	□ Grades	□ Behavior
	□ Homework	□ Class work
	□ Projects	□ Schedule Meeting
Notes/Other:		

Action to be Taken:

Contact Purpose	□ Glow	□ Grow

I'm too busy working on my own grass to notice if yours is greener.

Contact Documentation Form

Student Name: _____   Class: _____

Date and Time: _____   Person Initiating: _____

Person Contacted	□ Parent/Guardian:
	□ Counselor:
	□ Nurse:
	□ Administrator:
	□ Other:

Type of Contact	□ Phone Call/Text	□ Email
	□ Informal Meeting	□ Letter/Note
	□ Arranged Meeting	□ Class Dojo
	□ Other: _____	

Phone Call Response	□ No Answer	□ Wrong Number _____	□ Left Voicemail	□ Sent Text

Topic Discussed	□ Grades	□ Behavior
	□ Homework	□ Class work
	□ Projects	□ Schedule Meeting
Notes/Other:		

Action to be Taken:

Contact Purpose	□ Glow	□ Grow

You can totally do this!!

122

Contact Documentation Form

Student Name: _____   Class: _____

Date and Time: _____   Person Initiating: _____

Person Contacted	□ Parent/Guardian:
	□ Counselor:
	□ Nurse:
	□ Administrator:
	□ Other:

Type of Contact	□ Phone Call/Text	□ Email
	□ Informal Meeting	□ Letter/Note
	□ Arranged Meeting	□ Class Dojo
	□ Other: _____	

Phone Call Response	□ No Answer	□ Wrong Number _____	□ Left Voicemail	□ Sent Text

Topic Discussed	□ Grades	□ Behavior
	□ Homework	□ Class work
	□ Projects	□ Schedule Meeting
Notes/Other:		

Action to be Taken:

Contact Purpose	□ Glow	□ Grow

No pressure, No diamonds.

Contact Documentation Form

Student Name: _____   Class: _____

Date and Time: _____   Person Initiating: _____

Person Contacted	☐ Parent/Guardian:
	☐ Counselor:
	☐ Nurse:
	☐ Administrator:
	☐ Other:

Type of Contact	☐ Phone Call/Text	☐ Email
	☐ Informal Meeting	☐ Letter/Note
	☐ Arranged Meeting	☐ Class Dojo
	☐ Other: _____	

Phone Call Response	☐ No Answer	☐ Wrong Number _____	☐ Left Voicemail	☐ Sent Text

Topic Discussed	☐ Grades	☐ Behavior
	☐ Homework	☐ Class work
	☐ Projects	☐ Schedule Meeting

Notes/Other:

Action to be Taken:

Contact Purpose	☐ Glow	☐ Grow

Life is better when you're laughing...

Contact Documentation Form

Student Name: _____   Class: _____

Date and Time: _____   Person Initiating: _____

Person Contacted	□ Parent/Guardian:
	□ Counselor:
	□ Nurse:
	□ Administrator:
	□ Other:

Type of Contact	□ Phone Call/Text	□ Email
	□ Informal Meeting	□ Letter/Note
	□ Arranged Meeting	□ Class Dojo
	□ Other: _____	

Phone Call Response	□ No Answer	□ Wrong Number _____	□ Left Voicemail	□ Sent Text

Topic Discussed	□ Grades	□ Behavior
	□ Homework	□ Class work
	□ Projects	□ Schedule Meeting
Notes/Other:		

Action to be Taken:

Contact Purpose	□ Glow	□ Grow

If you want to fly, give up everything that weighs you down. - Budhha

Contact Documentation Form

Student Name: _____   Class: _____

Date and Time: _____   Person Initiating: _____

Person Contacted	☐ Parent/Guardian:
	☐ Counselor:
	☐ Nurse:
	☐ Administrator:
	☐ Other:

Type of Contact	☐ Phone Call/Text	☐ Email
	☐ Informal Meeting	☐ Letter/Note
	☐ Arranged Meeting	☐ Class Dojo
	☐ Other: _____	

Phone Call Response	☐ No Answer	☐ Wrong Number _____	☐ Left Voicemail	☐ Sent Text

Topic Discussed	☐ Grades	☐ Behavior
	☐ Homework	☐ Class work
	☐ Projects	☐ Schedule Meeting

Notes/Other:

Action to be Taken:

Contact Purpose	☐ Glow	☐ Grow

A smart person knows what to say; a wise person knows whether or not to say it.

Contact Documentation Form

Student Name: _____ Class: _____

Date and Time: _____ Person Initiating: _____

Person Contacted	□ Parent/Guardian:
	□ Counselor:
	□ Nurse:
	□ Administrator:
	□ Other:

Type of Contact	□ Phone Call/Text	□ Email
	□ Informal Meeting	□ Letter/Note
	□ Arranged Meeting	□ Class Dojo
	□ Other: _____	

Phone Call Response	□ No Answer	□ Wrong Number _____	□ Left Voicemail	□ Sent Text

Topic Discussed	□ Grades	□ Behavior
	□ Homework	□ Class work
	□ Projects	□ Schedule Meeting
Notes/Other:		

Action to be Taken:

Contact Purpose	□ Glow	□ Grow

Count your blessings. Name them one by one and see what the Lord has done.

Contact Documentation Form

Student Name: _____   Class: _____

Date and Time: _____   Person Initiating: _____

Person Contacted	☐ Parent/Guardian:
	☐ Counselor:
	☐ Nurse:
	☐ Administrator:
	☐ Other:

Type of Contact	☐ Phone Call/Text	☐ Email
	☐ Informal Meeting	☐ Letter/Note
	☐ Arranged Meeting	☐ Class Dojo
	☐ Other: _____	

Phone Call Response	☐ No Answer	☐ Wrong Number _____	☐ Left Voicemail	☐ Sent Text

Topic Discussed	☐ Grades	☐ Behavior
	☐ Homework	☐ Class work
	☐ Projects	☐ Schedule Meeting
Notes/Other:		

Action to be Taken:

Contact Purpose	☐ Glow	☐ Grow

No rain. No flowers.

Contact Documentation Form

Student Name: _____   Class: _____

Date and Time: _____   Person Initiating: _____

Person Contacted	☐ Parent/Guardian:	
	☐ Counselor:	
	☐ Nurse:	
	☐ Administrator:	
	☐ Other:	

Type of Contact	☐ Phone Call/Text	☐ Email
	☐ Informal Meeting	☐ Letter/Note
	☐ Arranged Meeting	☐ Class Dojo
	☐ Other: _____	

Phone Call Response	☐ No Answer	☐ Wrong Number _____	☐ Left Voicemail	☐ Sent Text

Topic Discussed	☐ Grades	☐ Behavior
	☐ Homework	☐ Class work
	☐ Projects	☐ Schedule Meeting
Notes/Other:		

Action to be Taken:

Contact Purpose	☐ Glow	☐ Grow

NEVER DULL YOUR SUNSHINE FOR SOMEONE ELSE.

Contact Documentation Form

Student Name: _____   Class: _____

Date and Time: _____   Person Initiating: _____

Person Contacted	☐ Parent/Guardian:
	☐ Counselor:
	☐ Nurse:
	☐ Administrator:
	☐ Other:

Type of Contact	☐ Phone Call/Text	☐ Email
	☐ Informal Meeting	☐ Letter/Note
	☐ Arranged Meeting	☐ Class Dojo
	☐ Other: _____	

Phone Call Response	☐ No Answer	☐ Wrong Number _____	☐ Left Voicemail	☐ Sent Text

Topic Discussed	☐ Grades	☐ Behavior
	☐ Homework	☐ Class work
	☐ Projects	☐ Schedule Meeting
Notes/Other:		

Action to be Taken:

Contact Purpose	☐ Glow	☐ Grow

Life is too short to wait until tomorrow.

Contact Documentation Form

Student Name: _____ Class: _____

Date and Time: _____ Person Initiating: _____

Person Contacted	□ Parent/Guardian:
	□ Counselor:
	□ Nurse:
	□ Administrator:
	□ Other:

Type of Contact	□ Phone Call/Text	□ Email
	□ Informal Meeting	□ Letter/Note
	□ Arranged Meeting	□ Class Dojo
	□ Other: _____	

Phone Call Response	□ No Answer	□ Wrong Number _____	□ Left Voicemail	□ Sent Text

Topic Discussed	□ Grades	□ Behavior
	□ Homework	□ Class work
	□ Projects	□ Schedule Meeting
Notes/Other:		

Action to be Taken:

Contact Purpose	□ Glow	□ Grow

Life is a onetime offer. Use it well.

Contact Documentation Form

Student Name: _____   Class: _____

Date and Time: _____   Person Initiating: _____

Person Contacted	☐ Parent/Guardian:
	☐ Counselor:
	☐ Nurse:
	☐ Administrator:
	☐ Other:

Type of Contact	☐ Phone Call/Text	☐ Email
	☐ Informal Meeting	☐ Letter/Note
	☐ Arranged Meeting	☐ Class Dojo
	☐ Other: _____	

Phone Call Response	☐ No Answer	☐ Wrong Number _____	☐ Left Voicemail	☐ Sent Text

Topic Discussed	☐ Grades	☐ Behavior
	☐ Homework	☐ Class work
	☐ Projects	☐ Schedule Meeting
Notes/Other:		

Action to be Taken:

Contact Purpose	☐ Glow	☐ Grow

Nothing changes if nothing changes.

Contact Documentation Form

Student Name: _____   Class: _____

Date and Time: _____   Person Initiating: _____

Person Contacted	
	□ Parent/Guardian:
	□ Counselor:
	□ Nurse:
	□ Administrator:
	□ Other:

Type of Contact		
	□ Phone Call/Text	□ Email
	□ Informal Meeting	□ Letter/Note
	□ Arranged Meeting	□ Class Dojo
	□ Other: _____	

Phone Call Response	□ No Answer	□ Wrong Number _____	□ Left Voicemail	□ Sent Text

Topic Discussed		
	□ Grades	□ Behavior
	□ Homework	□ Class work
	□ Projects	□ Schedule Meeting
Notes/Other:		

Action to be Taken:

Contact Purpose	□ Glow	□ Grow

Sometimes you have to keep good news to yourself. Everybody is not genuinely happy for you.

Contact Documentation Form

Student Name: _____   Class: _____

Date and Time: _____   Person Initiating: _____

Person Contacted	☐ Parent/Guardian:	
	☐ Counselor:	
	☐ Nurse:	
	☐ Administrator:	
	☐ Other:	

Type of Contact	☐ Phone Call/Text	☐ Email
	☐ Informal Meeting	☐ Letter/Note
	☐ Arranged Meeting	☐ Class Dojo
	☐ Other: _____	

Phone Call Response	☐ No Answer	☐ Wrong Number _____	☐ Left Voicemail	☐ Sent Text

Topic Discussed	☐ Grades	☐ Behavior
	☐ Homework	☐ Class work
	☐ Projects	☐ Schedule Meeting
Notes/Other:		

Action to be Taken:

Contact Purpose	☐ Glow	☐ Grow

If someone doesn't appreciate your presence, make them appreciate your absence.

Contact Documentation Form

Student Name: _____   Class: _____

Date and Time: _____   Person Initiating: _____

Person Contacted	□ Parent/Guardian:
	□ Counselor:
	□ Nurse:
	□ Administrator:
	□ Other:

Type of Contact	□ Phone Call/Text	□ Email
	□ Informal Meeting	□ Letter/Note
	□ Arranged Meeting	□ Class Dojo
	□ Other: _____	

Phone Call Response	□ No Answer	□ Wrong Number _____	□ Left Voicemail	□ Sent Text

Topic Discussed	□ Grades	□ Behavior
	□ Homework	□ Class work
	□ Projects	□ Schedule Meeting
Notes/Other:		

Action to be Taken:

Contact Purpose	□ Glow	□ Grow

Do more of what makes you happy.

Contact Documentation Form

Student Name: _____   Class: _____

Date and Time: _____   Person Initiating: _____

Person Contacted	☐ Parent/Guardian:
	☐ Counselor:
	☐ Nurse:
	☐ Administrator:
	☐ Other:

Type of Contact	☐ Phone Call/Text	☐ Email
	☐ Informal Meeting	☐ Letter/Note
	☐ Arranged Meeting	☐ Class Dojo
	☐ Other: _____	

Phone Call Response	☐ No Answer	☐ Wrong Number _____	☐ Left Voicemail	☐ Sent Text

Topic Discussed	☐ Grades	☐ Behavior
	☐ Homework	☐ Class work
	☐ Projects	☐ Schedule Meeting
Notes/Other:		

Action to be Taken:

Contact Purpose	☐ Glow	☐ Grow

Every master was once a beginner.

Contact Documentation Form

Student Name: _____ Class: _____

Date and Time: _____ Person Initiating: _____

Person Contacted	□ Parent/Guardian:	
	□ Counselor:	
	□ Nurse:	
	□ Administrator:	
	□ Other:	

Type of Contact	□ Phone Call/Text	□ Email
	□ Informal Meeting	□ Letter/Note
	□ Arranged Meeting	□ Class Dojo
	□ Other: _____	

Phone Call Response	□ No Answer	□ Wrong Number _____	□ Left Voicemail	□ Sent Text

Topic Discussed	□ Grades	□ Behavior
	□ Homework	□ Class work
	□ Projects	□ Schedule Meeting
Notes/Other:		

Action to be Taken:

Contact Purpose	□ Glow	□ Grow

Don't hold on to thoughts that don't allow your mind to move forward.

Contact Documentation Form

Student Name: _____   Class: _____

Date and Time: _____   Person Initiating: _____

Person Contacted	☐ Parent/Guardian:
	☐ Counselor:
	☐ Nurse:
	☐ Administrator:
	☐ Other:

Type of Contact	☐ Phone Call/Text	☐ Email
	☐ Informal Meeting	☐ Letter/Note
	☐ Arranged Meeting	☐ Class Dojo
	☐ Other: _____	

Phone Call Response	☐ No Answer	☐ Wrong Number _____	☐ Left Voicemail	☐ Sent Text

Topic Discussed	☐ Grades	☐ Behavior
	☐ Homework	☐ Class work
	☐ Projects	☐ Schedule Meeting
Notes/Other:		

Action to be Taken:

Contact Purpose	☐ Glow	☐ Grow

NOTE TO SELF: STOP TRYING SO HARD FOR PEOPLE WHO DON'T CARE.

Contact Documentation Form

Student Name: _____   Class: _____

Date and Time: _____   Person Initiating: _____

Person Contacted	☐ Parent/Guardian:
	☐ Counselor:
	☐ Nurse:
	☐ Administrator:
	☐ Other:

Type of Contact	☐ Phone Call/Text	☐ Email
	☐ Informal Meeting	☐ Letter/Note
	☐ Arranged Meeting	☐ Class Dojo
	☐ Other: _____	

Phone Call Response	☐ No Answer	☐ Wrong Number _____	☐ Left Voicemail	☐ Sent Text

Topic Discussed	☐ Grades	☐ Behavior
	☐ Homework	☐ Class work
	☐ Projects	☐ Schedule Meeting
Notes/Other:		

Action to be Taken:

Contact Purpose	☐ Glow	☐ Grow

Many a false step is made by standing still.

Contact Documentation Form

Student Name: _____   Class: _____

Date and Time: _____   Person Initiating: _____

Person Contacted	□ Parent/Guardian:
	□ Counselor:
	□ Nurse:
	□ Administrator:
	□ Other:

Type of Contact	□ Phone Call/Text	□ Email
	□ Informal Meeting	□ Letter/Note
	□ Arranged Meeting	□ Class Dojo
	□ Other: _____	

Phone Call Response	□ No Answer	□ Wrong Number _____	□ Left Voicemail	□ Sent Text

Topic Discussed	□ Grades	□ Behavior
	□ Homework	□ Class work
	□ Projects	□ Schedule Meeting
Notes/Other:		

Action to be Taken:

Contact Purpose	□ Glow	□ Grow

Know God, Know Peace.

Contact Documentation Form

Student Name: _____   Class: _____

Date and Time: _____   Person Initiating: _____

Person Contacted	
	☐ Parent/Guardian:
	☐ Counselor:
	☐ Nurse:
	☐ Administrator:
	☐ Other:

Type of Contact		
	☐ Phone Call/Text	☐ Email
	☐ Informal Meeting	☐ Letter/Note
	☐ Arranged Meeting	☐ Class Dojo
	☐ Other: _____	

Phone Call Response	☐ No Answer	☐ Wrong Number _____	☐ Left Voicemail	☐ Sent Text

Topic Discussed		
	☐ Grades	☐ Behavior
	☐ Homework	☐ Class work
	☐ Projects	☐ Schedule Meeting
Notes/Other:		

Action to be Taken:

Contact Purpose	☐ Glow	☐ Grow

Accept everything you are and nothing you are not.

Contact Documentation Form

Student Name: _____   Class: _____

Date and Time: _____   Person Initiating: _____

Person Contacted	☐ Parent/Guardian:
	☐ Counselor:
	☐ Nurse:
	☐ Administrator:
	☐ Other:

Type of Contact	☐ Phone Call/Text	☐ Email
	☐ Informal Meeting	☐ Letter/Note
	☐ Arranged Meeting	☐ Class Dojo
	☐ Other: _____	

Phone Call Response	☐ No Answer	☐ Wrong Number _____	☐ Left Voicemail	☐ Sent Text

Topic Discussed	☐ Grades	☐ Behavior
	☐ Homework	☐ Class work
	☐ Projects	☐ Schedule Meeting
Notes/Other:		

Action to be Taken:

Contact Purpose	☐ Glow	☐ Grow

This will make perfect sense one day.

Contact Documentation Form

Student Name: _____ Class: _____

Date and Time: _____ Person Initiating: _____

Person Contacted	□ Parent/Guardian:
	□ Counselor:
	□ Nurse:
	□ Administrator:
	□ Other:

Type of Contact	□ Phone Call/Text	□ Email
	□ Informal Meeting	□ Letter/Note
	□ Arranged Meeting	□ Class Dojo
	□ Other: _____	

Phone Call Response	□ No Answer	□ Wrong Number _____	□ Left Voicemail	□ Sent Text

Topic Discussed	□ Grades	□ Behavior
	□ Homework	□ Class work
	□ Projects	□ Schedule Meeting
Notes/Other:		

Action to be Taken:

Contact Purpose	□ Glow	□ Grow

Remember to live.

143

Contact Documentation Form

Student Name: _____   Class: _____

Date and Time: _____   Person Initiating: _____

Person Contacted	□ Parent/Guardian:
	□ Counselor:
	□ Nurse:
	□ Administrator:
	□ Other:

Type of Contact	□ Phone Call/Text	□ Email
	□ Informal Meeting	□ Letter/Note
	□ Arranged Meeting	□ Class Dojo
	□ Other: _____	

Phone Call Response	□ No Answer	□ Wrong Number _____	□ Left Voicemail	□ Sent Text

Topic Discussed	□ Grades	□ Behavior
	□ Homework	□ Class work
	□ Projects	□ Schedule Meeting
Notes/Other:		

Action to be Taken:

Contact Purpose	□ Glow	□ Grow

It's okay if the only thing you did today was breathe.

Contact Documentation Form

Student Name: _____ Class: _____

Date and Time: _____ Person Initiating: _____

Person Contacted	☐ Parent/Guardian:
	☐ Counselor:
	☐ Nurse:
	☐ Administrator:
	☐ Other:

Type of Contact	☐ Phone Call/Text	☐ Email
	☐ Informal Meeting	☐ Letter/Note
	☐ Arranged Meeting	☐ Class Dojo
	☐ Other: _____	

Phone Call Response	☐ No Answer	☐ Wrong Number _____	☐ Left Voicemail	☐ Sent Text

Topic Discussed	☐ Grades	☐ Behavior
	☐ Homework	☐ Class work
	☐ Projects	☐ Schedule Meeting
Notes/Other:		

Action to be Taken:

Contact Purpose	☐ Glow	☐ Grow

Be selective in your battles. Sometimes peace is better than being right.

Contact Documentation Form

Student Name: _____ Class: _____

Date and Time: _____ Person Initiating: _____

Person Contacted	☐ Parent/Guardian:
	☐ Counselor:
	☐ Nurse:
	☐ Administrator:
	☐ Other:

Type of Contact	☐ Phone Call/Text	☐ Email
	☐ Informal Meeting	☐ Letter/Note
	☐ Arranged Meeting	☐ Class Dojo
	☐ Other: _____	

Phone Call Response	☐ No Answer	☐ Wrong Number _____	☐ Left Voicemail	☐ Sent Text

Topic Discussed	☐ Grades	☐ Behavior
	☐ Homework	☐ Class work
	☐ Projects	☐ Schedule Meeting

Notes/Other:

Action to be Taken:

Contact Purpose	☐ Glow	☐ Grow

Why follow when you can LEAD.

Contact Documentation Form

Student Name: _____ Class: _____

Date and Time: _____ Person Initiating: _____

Person Contacted	☐ Parent/Guardian:
	☐ Counselor:
	☐ Nurse:
	☐ Administrator:
	☐ Other:

Type of Contact	☐ Phone Call/Text	☐ Email
	☐ Informal Meeting	☐ Letter/Note
	☐ Arranged Meeting	☐ Class Dojo
	☐ Other: _____	

Phone Call Response	☐ No Answer	☐ Wrong Number _____	☐ Left Voicemail	☐ Sent Text

Topic Discussed	☐ Grades	☐ Behavior
	☐ Homework	☐ Class work
	☐ Projects	☐ Schedule Meeting
Notes/Other:		

Action to be Taken:

Contact Purpose	☐ Glow	☐ Grow

Carpe Diem.

Contact Documentation Form

Student Name: _____   Class: _____

Date and Time: _____   Person Initiating: _____

Person Contacted	☐ Parent/Guardian:
	☐ Counselor:
	☐ Nurse:
	☐ Administrator:
	☐ Other:

Type of Contact	☐ Phone Call/Text	☐ Email
	☐ Informal Meeting	☐ Letter/Note
	☐ Arranged Meeting	☐ Class Dojo
	☐ Other: _____	

Phone Call Response	☐ No Answer	☐ Wrong Number _____	☐ Left Voicemail	☐ Sent Text

Topic Discussed	☐ Grades	☐ Behavior
	☐ Homework	☐ Class work
	☐ Projects	☐ Schedule Meeting
Notes/Other:		

Action to be Taken:

Contact Purpose	☐ Glow	☐ Grow

Still I rise.

Contact Documentation Form

Student Name: _____ Class: _____

Date and Time: _____ Person Initiating: _____

Person Contacted	□ Parent/Guardian:
	□ Counselor:
	□ Nurse:
	□ Administrator:
	□ Other:

Type of Contact	□ Phone Call/Text	□ Email
	□ Informal Meeting	□ Letter/Note
	□ Arranged Meeting	□ Class Dojo
	□ Other: _____	

Phone Call Response	□ No Answer	□ Wrong Number _____	□ Left Voicemail	□ Sent Text

Topic Discussed	□ Grades	□ Behavior
	□ Homework	□ Class work
	□ Projects	□ Schedule Meeting
Notes/Other:		

Action to be Taken:

Contact Purpose	□ Glow	□ Grow

Coffee and kindness…maybe two coffees and then kindness.

Contact Documentation Form

Student Name: _____   Class: _____

Date and Time: _____   Person Initiating: _____

Person Contacted	☐ Parent/Guardian:
	☐ Counselor:
	☐ Nurse:
	☐ Administrator:
	☐ Other:

Type of Contact	☐ Phone Call/Text	☐ Email
	☐ Informal Meeting	☐ Letter/Note
	☐ Arranged Meeting	☐ Class Dojo
	☐ Other: _____	

Phone Call Response	☐ No Answer	☐ Wrong Number _____	☐ Left Voicemail	☐ Sent Text

Topic Discussed	☐ Grades	☐ Behavior
	☐ Homework	☐ Class work
	☐ Projects	☐ Schedule Meeting
Notes/Other:		

Action to be Taken:

Contact Purpose	☐ Glow	☐ Grow

THE DREAM IS FREE. THE HUSTLE IS SOLD SEPARATELY.

Contact Documentation Form

Student Name: _____ Class: _____

Date and Time: _____ Person Initiating: _____

Person Contacted	☐ Parent/Guardian:
	☐ Counselor:
	☐ Nurse:
	☐ Administrator:
	☐ Other:

Type of Contact	☐ Phone Call/Text	☐ Email
	☐ Informal Meeting	☐ Letter/Note
	☐ Arranged Meeting	☐ Class Dojo
	☐ Other: _____	

Phone Call Response	☐ No Answer	☐ Wrong Number _____	☐ Left Voicemail	☐ Sent Text

Topic Discussed	☐ Grades	☐ Behavior
	☐ Homework	☐ Class work
	☐ Projects	☐ Schedule Meeting
Notes/Other:		

Action to be Taken:

Contact Purpose	☐ Glow	☐ Grow

Stay strong. Your story isn't over yet.

Contact Documentation Form

Student Name: _____   Class: _____

Date and Time: _____   Person Initiating: _____

Person Contacted	☐ Parent/Guardian:
	☐ Counselor:
	☐ Nurse:
	☐ Administrator:
	☐ Other:

Type of Contact	☐ Phone Call/Text	☐ Email
	☐ Informal Meeting	☐ Letter/Note
	☐ Arranged Meeting	☐ Class Dojo
	☐ Other: _____	

Phone Call Response	☐ No Answer	☐ Wrong Number _____	☐ Left Voicemail	☐ Sent Text

Topic Discussed	☐ Grades	☐ Behavior
	☐ Homework	☐ Class work
	☐ Projects	☐ Schedule Meeting
Notes/Other:		

Action to be Taken:

Contact Purpose	☐ Glow	☐ Grow

Smile and walk away.

Contact Documentation Form

Student Name: _____   Class: _____

Date and Time: _____   Person Initiating: _____

Person Contacted	☐ Parent/Guardian:
	☐ Counselor:
	☐ Nurse:
	☐ Administrator:
	☐ Other:

Type of Contact	☐ Phone Call/Text	☐ Email
	☐ Informal Meeting	☐ Letter/Note
	☐ Arranged Meeting	☐ Class Dojo
	☐ Other: _____	

Phone Call Response	☐ No Answer	☐ Wrong Number _____	☐ Left Voicemail	☐ Sent Text

Topic Discussed	☐ Grades	☐ Behavior
	☐ Homework	☐ Class work
	☐ Projects	☐ Schedule Meeting
Notes/Other:		

Action to be Taken:

Contact Purpose	☐ Glow	☐ Grow

Let gratitude be your attitude.

Contact Documentation Form

Student Name: _____ Class: _____

Date and Time: _____ Person Initiating: _____

Person Contacted	□ Parent/Guardian:
	□ Counselor:
	□ Nurse:
	□ Administrator:
	□ Other:

Type of Contact	□ Phone Call/Text	□ Email
	□ Informal Meeting	□ Letter/Note
	□ Arranged Meeting	□ Class Dojo
	□ Other: _____	

Phone Call Response	□ No Answer	□ Wrong Number _____	□ Left Voicemail	□ Sent Text

Topic Discussed	□ Grades	□ Behavior
	□ Homework	□ Class work
	□ Projects	□ Schedule Meeting
Notes/Other:		

Action to be Taken:

Contact Purpose	□ Glow	□ Grow

If you want the rainbow, you have to deal with the rain.

Contact Documentation Form

Student Name: _____   Class: _____

Date and Time: _____   Person Initiating: _____

Person Contacted	□ Parent/Guardian:
	□ Counselor:
	□ Nurse:
	□ Administrator:
	□ Other:

Type of Contact	□ Phone Call/Text	□ Email
	□ Informal Meeting	□ Letter/Note
	□ Arranged Meeting	□ Class Dojo
	□ Other: _____	

Phone Call Response	□ No Answer	□ Wrong Number _____	□ Left Voicemail	□ Sent Text

Topic Discussed	□ Grades	□ Behavior
	□ Homework	□ Class work
	□ Projects	□ Schedule Meeting
Notes/Other:		

Action to be Taken:

Contact Purpose	□ Glow	□ Grow

But God!

School Year

Contact Documentation Form

Student Name: _____   Class: _____

Date and Time: _____   Person Initiating: _____

Person Contacted	□ Parent/Guardian:	
	□ Counselor:	
	□ Nurse:	
	□ Administrator:	
	□ Other:	

Type of Contact	□ Phone Call/Text	□ Email
	□ Informal Meeting	□ Letter/Note
	□ Arranged Meeting	□ Class Dojo
	□ Other: _____	

Phone Call Response	□ No Answer	□ Wrong Number _____	□ Left Voicemail	□ Sent Text

Topic Discussed	□ Grades	□ Behavior
	□ Homework	□ Class work
	□ Projects	□ Schedule Meeting
Notes/Other:		

Action to be Taken:

Contact Purpose	□ Glow	□ Grow

Life has 2 rules. #1-Never Quit #2-Always remember rule #1 — Unknown

Contact Documentation Form

Student Name: _____   Class: _____

Date and Time: _____   Person Initiating: _____

Person Contacted	☐ Parent/Guardian:	
	☐ Counselor:	
	☐ Nurse:	
	☐ Administrator:	
	☐ Other:	

Type of Contact	☐ Phone Call/Text	☐ Email
	☐ Informal Meeting	☐ Letter/Note
	☐ Arranged Meeting	☐ Class Dojo
	☐ Other: _____	

Phone Call Response	☐ No Answer	☐ Wrong Number _____	☐ Left Voicemail	☐ Sent Text

Topic Discussed	☐ Grades	☐ Behavior
	☐ Homework	☐ Class work
	☐ Projects	☐ Schedule Meeting

Notes/Other:

Action to be Taken:

Contact Purpose	☐ Glow	☐ Grow

Out of a mountain of despair, a stone of hope. — Martin Luther King, Jr.

Contact Documentation Form

Student Name: _____   Class: _____

Date and Time: _____   Person Initiating: _____

Person Contacted	☐ Parent/Guardian:
	☐ Counselor:
	☐ Nurse:
	☐ Administrator:
	☐ Other:

Type of Contact	☐ Phone Call/Text	☐ Email
	☐ Informal Meeting	☐ Letter/Note
	☐ Arranged Meeting	☐ Class Dojo
	☐ Other: _____	

Phone Call Response	☐ No Answer	☐ Wrong Number _____	☐ Left Voicemail	☐ Sent Text

Topic Discussed	☐ Grades	☐ Behavior
	☐ Homework	☐ Class work
	☐ Projects	☐ Schedule Meeting
Notes/Other:		

Action to be Taken:

Contact Purpose	☐ Glow	☐ Grow

Act as if what you do makes a difference. IT DOES. – *William James*

Contact Documentation Form

Student Name: _____   Class: _____

Date and Time: _____   Person Initiating: _____

Person Contacted	□ Parent/Guardian:
	□ Counselor:
	□ Nurse:
	□ Administrator:
	□ Other:

Type of Contact	□ Phone Call/Text	□ Email
	□ Informal Meeting	□ Letter/Note
	□ Arranged Meeting	□ Class Dojo
	□ Other: _____	

Phone Call Response	□ No Answer	□ Wrong Number _____	□ Left Voicemail	□ Sent Text

Topic Discussed	□ Grades	□ Behavior
	□ Homework	□ Class work
	□ Projects	□ Schedule Meeting
Notes/Other:		

Action to be Taken:

Contact Purpose	□ Glow	□ Grow

Nothing is impossible. The word itself says "I'm possible!" – *Audrey Hepburn*

Contact Documentation Form

Student Name: _____ Class: _____

Date and Time: _____ Person Initiating: _____

Person Contacted	□ Parent/Guardian:
	□ Counselor:
	□ Nurse:
	□ Administrator:
	□ Other:

Type of Contact	□ Phone Call/Text	□ Email
	□ Informal Meeting	□ Letter/Note
	□ Arranged Meeting	□ Class Dojo
	□ Other: _____	

Phone Call Response	□ No Answer	□ Wrong Number _____	□ Left Voicemail	□ Sent Text

Topic Discussed	□ Grades	□ Behavior
	□ Homework	□ Class work
	□ Projects	□ Schedule Meeting
Notes/Other:		

Action to be Taken:

Contact Purpose	□ Glow	□ Grow

Try to be a rainbow in someone else's cloud. — *Maya Angelou.*

Contact Documentation Form

Student Name: _____   Class: _____

Date and Time: _____   Person Initiating: _____

Person Contacted	☐ Parent/Guardian:
	☐ Counselor:
	☐ Nurse:
	☐ Administrator:
	☐ Other:

Type of Contact	☐ Phone Call/Text	☐ Email
	☐ Informal Meeting	☐ Letter/Note
	☐ Arranged Meeting	☐ Class Dojo
	☐ Other: _____	

Phone Call Response	☐ No Answer	☐ Wrong Number _____	☐ Left Voicemail	☐ Sent Text

Topic Discussed	☐ Grades	☐ Behavior
	☐ Homework	☐ Class work
	☐ Projects	☐ Schedule Meeting
Notes/Other:		

Action to be Taken:

Contact Purpose	☐ Glow	☐ Grow

You are enough just as you are. — Megan Markle

Contact Documentation Form

Student Name: _____   Class: _____

Date and Time: _____   Person Initiating: _____

Person Contacted	☐ Parent/Guardian:
	☐ Counselor:
	☐ Nurse:
	☐ Administrator:
	☐ Other:

Type of Contact	☐ Phone Call/Text	☐ Email
	☐ Informal Meeting	☐ Letter/Note
	☐ Arranged Meeting	☐ Class Dojo
	☐ Other: _____	

Phone Call Response	☐ No Answer	☐ Wrong Number _____	☐ Left Voicemail	☐ Sent Text

Topic Discussed	☐ Grades	☐ Behavior
	☐ Homework	☐ Class work
	☐ Projects	☐ Schedule Meeting
Notes/Other:		

Action to be Taken:

Contact Purpose	☐ Glow	☐ Grow

Leadership is about making others better as a result of your presence and making sure that impact lasts in your absence. - Unknown

Contact Documentation Form

Student Name: _____ Class: _____

Date and Time: _____ Person Initiating: _____

Person Contacted	☐ Parent/Guardian:
	☐ Counselor:
	☐ Nurse:
	☐ Administrator:
	☐ Other:

Type of Contact	☐ Phone Call/Text	☐ Email
	☐ Informal Meeting	☐ Letter/Note
	☐ Arranged Meeting	☐ Class Dojo
	☐ Other: _____	

Phone Call Response	☐ No Answer	☐ Wrong Number _____	☐ Left Voicemail	☐ Sent Text

Topic Discussed	☐ Grades	☐ Behavior
	☐ Homework	☐ Class work
	☐ Projects	☐ Schedule Meeting
Notes/Other:		

Action to be Taken:

Contact Purpose	☐ Glow	☐ Grow

Be a Pineapple. Stand tall. Wear a Crown. and Be sweet on the inside. - Unknown

Contact Documentation Form

Student Name: _____ Class: _____

Date and Time: _____ Person Initiating: _____

Person Contacted	☐ Parent/Guardian:
	☐ Counselor:
	☐ Nurse:
	☐ Administrator:
	☐ Other:

Type of Contact	☐ Phone Call/Text	☐ Email
	☐ Informal Meeting	☐ Letter/Note
	☐ Arranged Meeting	☐ Class Dojo
	☐ Other: _____	

Phone Call Response	☐ No Answer	☐ Wrong Number _____	☐ Left Voicemail	☐ Sent Text

Topic Discussed	☐ Grades	☐ Behavior
	☐ Homework	☐ Class work
	☐ Projects	☐ Schedule Meeting
Notes/Other:		

Action to be Taken:

Contact Purpose	☐ Glow	☐ Grow

The first step to getting somewhere is to decide you're not going to stay where you are. – J.P. Morgan

Contact Documentation Form

Student Name: _____   Class: _____

Date and Time: _____   Person Initiating: _____

Person Contacted	☐ Parent/Guardian:
	☐ Counselor:
	☐ Nurse:
	☐ Administrator:
	☐ Other:

Type of Contact	☐ Phone Call/Text	☐ Email
	☐ Informal Meeting	☐ Letter/Note
	☐ Arranged Meeting	☐ Class Dojo
	☐ Other: _____	

Phone Call Response	☐ No Answer	☐ Wrong Number _____	☐ Left Voicemail	☐ Sent Text

Topic Discussed	☐ Grades	☐ Behavior
	☐ Homework	☐ Class work
	☐ Projects	☐ Schedule Meeting
Notes/Other:		

Action to be Taken:

Contact Purpose	☐ Glow	☐ Grow

You can't go back and change the beginning but you can start where you are and change the ending. – C.S. Lewis

Contact Documentation Form

Student Name: _____   Class: _____

Date and Time: _____   Person Initiating: _____

Person Contacted	□ Parent/Guardian:
	□ Counselor:
	□ Nurse:
	□ Administrator:
	□ Other:

Type of Contact	□ Phone Call/Text	□ Email
	□ Informal Meeting	□ Letter/Note
	□ Arranged Meeting	□ Class Dojo
	□ Other: _____	

Phone Call Response	□ No Answer	□ Wrong Number _____	□ Left Voicemail	□ Sent Text

Topic Discussed	□ Grades	□ Behavior
	□ Homework	□ Class work
	□ Projects	□ Schedule Meeting
Notes/Other:		

Action to be Taken:

Contact Purpose	□ Glow	□ Grow

Believe in yourself a little more.

Contact Documentation Form

Student Name: _____   Class: _____

Date and Time: _____   Person Initiating: _____

Person Contacted	☐ Parent/Guardian:
	☐ Counselor:
	☐ Nurse:
	☐ Administrator:
	☐ Other:

Type of Contact	☐ Phone Call/Text	☐ Email
	☐ Informal Meeting	☐ Letter/Note
	☐ Arranged Meeting	☐ Class Dojo
	☐ Other: _____	

Phone Call Response	☐ No Answer	☐ Wrong Number _____	☐ Left Voicemail	☐ Sent Text

Topic Discussed	☐ Grades	☐ Behavior
	☐ Homework	☐ Class work
	☐ Projects	☐ Schedule Meeting
Notes/Other:		

Action to be Taken:

Contact Purpose	☐ Glow	☐ Grow

There is only one corner of the universe you can be certain improving and that's your own self.

-Aldous Huxley

Contact Documentation Form

Student Name: _____ Class: _____

Date and Time: _____ Person Initiating: _____

Person Contacted	□ Parent/Guardian:
	□ Counselor:
	□ Nurse:
	□ Administrator:
	□ Other:

Type of Contact	□ Phone Call/Text	□ Email
	□ Informal Meeting	□ Letter/Note
	□ Arranged Meeting	□ Class Dojo
	□ Other: _____	

Phone Call Response	□ No Answer	□ Wrong Number _____	□ Left Voicemail	□ Sent Text

Topic Discussed	□ Grades	□ Behavior
	□ Homework	□ Class work
	□ Projects	□ Schedule Meeting
Notes/Other:		

Action to be Taken:

Contact Purpose	□ Glow	□ Grow

A thousand mistakes are an education if you learn something from every one of them.

Contact Documentation Form

Student Name: _____   Class: _____

Date and Time: _____   Person Initiating: _____

Person Contacted	☐ Parent/Guardian:
	☐ Counselor:
	☐ Nurse:
	☐ Administrator:
	☐ Other:

Type of Contact	☐ Phone Call/Text	☐ Email
	☐ Informal Meeting	☐ Letter/Note
	☐ Arranged Meeting	☐ Class Dojo
	☐ Other: _____	

Phone Call Response	☐ No Answer	☐ Wrong Number _____	☐ Left Voicemail	☐ Sent Text

Topic Discussed	☐ Grades	☐ Behavior
	☐ Homework	☐ Class work
	☐ Projects	☐ Schedule Meeting

Notes/Other:

Action to be Taken:

Contact Purpose	☐ Glow	☐ Grow

I can. I will. End of story.

Contact Documentation Form

Student Name: _____   Class: _____

Date and Time: _____   Person Initiating: _____

Person Contacted	☐ Parent/Guardian:
	☐ Counselor:
	☐ Nurse:
	☐ Administrator:
	☐ Other:

Type of Contact	☐ Phone Call/Text	☐ Email
	☐ Informal Meeting	☐ Letter/Note
	☐ Arranged Meeting	☐ Class Dojo
	☐ Other: _____	

Phone Call Response	☐ No Answer	☐ Wrong Number _____	☐ Left Voicemail	☐ Sent Text

Topic Discussed	☐ Grades	☐ Behavior
	☐ Homework	☐ Class work
	☐ Projects	☐ Schedule Meeting
Notes/Other:		

Action to be Taken:

Contact Purpose	☐ Glow	☐ Grow

You are capable of amazing things.

Contact Documentation Form

Student Name: _____   Class: _____

Date and Time: _____   Person Initiating: _____

Person Contacted	☐ Parent/Guardian:
	☐ Counselor:
	☐ Nurse:
	☐ Administrator:
	☐ Other:

Type of Contact	☐ Phone Call/Text	☐ Email
	☐ Informal Meeting	☐ Letter/Note
	☐ Arranged Meeting	☐ Class Dojo
	☐ Other: _____	

Phone Call Response	☐ No Answer	☐ Wrong Number _____	☐ Left Voicemail	☐ Sent Text

Topic Discussed	☐ Grades	☐ Behavior
	☐ Homework	☐ Class work
	☐ Projects	☐ Schedule Meeting
Notes/Other:		

Action to be Taken:

Contact Purpose	☐ Glow	☐ Grow

Be careful how you are talking to yourself because you are listening.

Contact Documentation Form

Student Name: _____   Class: _____

Date and Time: _____   Person Initiating: _____

Person Contacted	□ Parent/Guardian:	
	□ Counselor:	
	□ Nurse:	
	□ Administrator:	
	□ Other:	

Type of Contact	□ Phone Call/Text	□ Email
	□ Informal Meeting	□ Letter/Note
	□ Arranged Meeting	□ Class Dojo
	□ Other: _____	

Phone Call Response	□ No Answer	□ Wrong Number _____	□ Left Voicemail	□ Sent Text

Topic Discussed	□ Grades	□ Behavior
	□ Homework	□ Class work
	□ Projects	□ Schedule Meeting
Notes/Other:		

Action to be Taken:

Contact Purpose	□ Glow	□ Grow

I'm too busy working on my own grass to notice if yours is greener.

Contact Documentation Form

Student Name: _____ Class: _____

Date and Time: _____ Person Initiating: _____

Person Contacted	☐ Parent/Guardian:
	☐ Counselor:
	☐ Nurse:
	☐ Administrator:
	☐ Other:

Type of Contact	☐ Phone Call/Text	☐ Email
	☐ Informal Meeting	☐ Letter/Note
	☐ Arranged Meeting	☐ Class Dojo
	☐ Other: _____	

Phone Call Response	☐ No Answer	☐ Wrong Number _____	☐ Left Voicemail	☐ Sent Text

Topic Discussed	☐ Grades	☐ Behavior
	☐ Homework	☐ Class work
	☐ Projects	☐ Schedule Meeting

Notes/Other:

Action to be Taken:

Contact Purpose	☐ Glow	☐ Grow

You can totally do this!!

Contact Documentation Form

Student Name: _____   Class: _____

Date and Time: _____   Person Initiating: _____

Person Contacted	☐ Parent/Guardian:
	☐ Counselor:
	☐ Nurse:
	☐ Administrator:
	☐ Other:

Type of Contact	☐ Phone Call/Text	☐ Email
	☐ Informal Meeting	☐ Letter/Note
	☐ Arranged Meeting	☐ Class Dojo
	☐ Other: _____	

Phone Call Response	☐ No Answer	☐ Wrong Number _____	☐ Left Voicemail	☐ Sent Text

Topic Discussed	☐ Grades	☐ Behavior
	☐ Homework	☐ Class work
	☐ Projects	☐ Schedule Meeting
Notes/Other:		

Action to be Taken:

Contact Purpose	☐ Glow	☐ Grow

No pressure. No diamonds.

Contact Documentation Form

Student Name: _____   Class: _____

Date and Time: _____   Person Initiating: _____

Person Contacted	□ Parent/Guardian:
	□ Counselor:
	□ Nurse:
	□ Administrator:
	□ Other:

Type of Contact	□ Phone Call/Text	□ Email
	□ Informal Meeting	□ Letter/Note
	□ Arranged Meeting	□ Class Dojo
	□ Other: _____	

Phone Call Response	□ No Answer	□ Wrong Number _____	□ Left Voicemail	□ Sent Text

Topic Discussed	□ Grades	□ Behavior
	□ Homework	□ Class work
	□ Projects	□ Schedule Meeting
Notes/Other:		

Action to be Taken:

Contact Purpose	□ Glow	□ Grow

Life is better when you're laughing...

Contact Documentation Form

Student Name: _____   Class: _____

Date and Time: _____   Person Initiating: _____

Person Contacted	□ Parent/Guardian:
	□ Counselor:
	□ Nurse:
	□ Administrator:
	□ Other:

Type of Contact	□ Phone Call/Text	□ Email
	□ Informal Meeting	□ Letter/Note
	□ Arranged Meeting	□ Class Dojo
	□ Other: _____	

Phone Call Response	□ No Answer	□ Wrong Number _____	□ Left Voicemail	□ Sent Text

Topic Discussed	□ Grades	□ Behavior
	□ Homework	□ Class work
	□ Projects	□ Schedule Meeting
Notes/Other:		

Action to be Taken:

Contact Purpose	□ Glow	□ Grow

If you want to fly, give up everything that weighs you down. – Budhha

Contact Documentation Form

Student Name: _____   Class: _____

Date and Time: _____   Person Initiating: _____

Person Contacted	□ Parent/Guardian:
	□ Counselor:
	□ Nurse:
	□ Administrator:
	□ Other:

Type of Contact	□ Phone Call/Text	□ Email
	□ Informal Meeting	□ Letter/Note
	□ Arranged Meeting	□ Class Dojo
	□ Other: _____	

Phone Call Response	□ No Answer	□ Wrong Number _____	□ Left Voicemail	□ Sent Text

Topic Discussed	□ Grades	□ Behavior
	□ Homework	□ Class work
	□ Projects	□ Schedule Meeting
Notes/Other:		

Action to be Taken:

Contact Purpose	□ Glow	□ Grow

A smart person knows what to say; a wise person knows whether or not to say it.

Contact Documentation Form

Student Name: _____   Class: _____

Date and Time: _____   Person Initiating: _____

Person Contacted	☐ Parent/Guardian:
	☐ Counselor:
	☐ Nurse:
	☐ Administrator:
	☐ Other:

Type of Contact	☐ Phone Call/Text	☐ Email
	☐ Informal Meeting	☐ Letter/Note
	☐ Arranged Meeting	☐ Class Dojo
	☐ Other: _____	

Phone Call Response	☐ No Answer	☐ Wrong Number _____	☐ Left Voicemail	☐ Sent Text

Topic Discussed	☐ Grades	☐ Behavior
	☐ Homework	☐ Class work
	☐ Projects	☐ Schedule Meeting
Notes/Other:		

Action to be Taken:

Contact Purpose	☐ Glow	☐ Grow

Count your blessings. Name them one by one and see what the Lord has done.

Contact Documentation Form

Student Name: _____   Class: _____

Date and Time: _____   Person Initiating: _____

Person Contacted	☐ Parent/Guardian:	
	☐ Counselor:	
	☐ Nurse:	
	☐ Administrator:	
	☐ Other:	

Type of Contact	☐ Phone Call/Text	☐ Email
	☐ Informal Meeting	☐ Letter/Note
	☐ Arranged Meeting	☐ Class Dojo
	☐ Other: _____	

Phone Call Response	☐ No Answer	☐ Wrong Number _____	☐ Left Voicemail	☐ Sent Text

Topic Discussed	☐ Grades	☐ Behavior
	☐ Homework	☐ Class work
	☐ Projects	☐ Schedule Meeting

Notes/Other:

Action to be Taken:

Contact Purpose	☐ Glow	☐ Grow

No rain. No flowers.

Contact Documentation Form

Student Name: _____   Class: _____

Date and Time: _____   Person Initiating: _____

Person Contacted	☐ Parent/Guardian:
	☐ Counselor:
	☐ Nurse:
	☐ Administrator:
	☐ Other:

Type of Contact	☐ Phone Call/Text	☐ Email
	☐ Informal Meeting	☐ Letter/Note
	☐ Arranged Meeting	☐ Class Dojo
	☐ Other: _____	

Phone Call Response	☐ No Answer	☐ Wrong Number _____	☐ Left Voicemail	☐ Sent Text

Topic Discussed	☐ Grades	☐ Behavior
	☐ Homework	☐ Class work
	☐ Projects	☐ Schedule Meeting
Notes/Other:		

Action to be Taken:

Contact Purpose	☐ Glow	☐ Grow

NEVER DULL YOUR SUNSHINE FOR SOMEONE ELSE.

Contact Documentation Form

Student Name: _____ Class: _____

Date and Time: _____ Person Initiating: _____

Person Contacted	☐ Parent/Guardian:	
	☐ Counselor:	
	☐ Nurse:	
	☐ Administrator:	
	☐ Other:	

Type of Contact	☐ Phone Call/Text	☐ Email
	☐ Informal Meeting	☐ Letter/Note
	☐ Arranged Meeting	☐ Class Dojo
	☐ Other: _____	

Phone Call Response	☐ No Answer	☐ Wrong Number _____	☐ Left Voicemail	☐ Sent Text

Topic Discussed	☐ Grades	☐ Behavior
	☐ Homework	☐ Class work
	☐ Projects	☐ Schedule Meeting

Notes/Other:

Action to be Taken:

Contact Purpose	☐ Glow	☐ Grow

Life is too short to wait until tomorrow.

Contact Documentation Form

Student Name: _____   Class: _____

Date and Time: _____   Person Initiating: _____

Person Contacted	□ Parent/Guardian:
	□ Counselor:
	□ Nurse:
	□ Administrator:
	□ Other:

Type of Contact	□ Phone Call/Text	□ Email
	□ Informal Meeting	□ Letter/Note
	□ Arranged Meeting	□ Class Dojo
	□ Other: _____	

Phone Call Response	□ No Answer	□ Wrong Number _____	□ Left Voicemail	□ Sent Text

Topic Discussed	□ Grades	□ Behavior
	□ Homework	□ Class work
	□ Projects	□ Schedule Meeting
Notes/Other:		

Action to be Taken:

Contact Purpose	□ Glow	□ Grow

Life is a onetime offer. Use it well.

Contact Documentation Form

Student Name: _____   Class: _____

Date and Time: _____   Person Initiating: _____

Person Contacted	☐ Parent/Guardian:
	☐ Counselor:
	☐ Nurse:
	☐ Administrator:
	☐ Other:

Type of Contact	☐ Phone Call/Text	☐ Email
	☐ Informal Meeting	☐ Letter/Note
	☐ Arranged Meeting	☐ Class Dojo
	☐ Other: _____	

Phone Call Response	☐ No Answer	☐ Wrong Number _____	☐ Left Voicemail	☐ Sent Text

Topic Discussed	☐ Grades	☐ Behavior
	☐ Homework	☐ Class work
	☐ Projects	☐ Schedule Meeting
Notes/Other:		

Action to be Taken:

Contact Purpose	☐ Glow	☐ Grow

Nothing changes if nothing changes.

Contact Documentation Form

Student Name: _____   Class: _____

Date and Time: _____   Person Initiating: _____

Person Contacted	□ Parent/Guardian:
	□ Counselor:
	□ Nurse:
	□ Administrator:
	□ Other:

Type of Contact	□ Phone Call/Text	□ Email
	□ Informal Meeting	□ Letter/Note
	□ Arranged Meeting	□ Class Dojo
	□ Other: _____	

Phone Call Response	□ No Answer	□ Wrong Number _____	□ Left Voicemail	□ Sent Text

Topic Discussed	□ Grades	□ Behavior
	□ Homework	□ Class work
	□ Projects	□ Schedule Meeting
Notes/Other:		

Action to be Taken:

Contact Purpose	□ Glow	□ Grow

Sometimes you have to keep good news to yourself. Everybody is not genuinely happy for you.

Contact Documentation Form

Student Name: _____   Class: _____

Date and Time: _____   Person Initiating: _____

Person Contacted	☐ Parent/Guardian:
	☐ Counselor:
	☐ Nurse:
	☐ Administrator:
	☐ Other:

Type of Contact	☐ Phone Call/Text	☐ Email
	☐ Informal Meeting	☐ Letter/Note
	☐ Arranged Meeting	☐ Class Dojo
	☐ Other: _____	

Phone Call Response	☐ No Answer	☐ Wrong Number _____	☐ Left Voicemail	☐ Sent Text

Topic Discussed	☐ Grades	☐ Behavior
	☐ Homework	☐ Class work
	☐ Projects	☐ Schedule Meeting

Notes/Other:

Action to be Taken:

Contact Purpose	☐ Glow	☐ Grow

If someone doesn't appreciate your presence, make them appreciate your absence.

Contact Documentation Form

Student Name: _____   Class: _____

Date and Time: _____   Person Initiating: _____

Person Contacted	☐ Parent/Guardian:
	☐ Counselor:
	☐ Nurse:
	☐ Administrator:
	☐ Other:

Type of Contact	☐ Phone Call/Text	☐ Email
	☐ Informal Meeting	☐ Letter/Note
	☐ Arranged Meeting	☐ Class Dojo
	☐ Other:_____	

Phone Call Response	☐ No Answer	☐ Wrong Number _____	☐ Left Voicemail	☐ Sent Text

Topic Discussed	☐ Grades	☐ Behavior
	☐ Homework	☐ Class work
	☐ Projects	☐ Schedule Meeting
Notes/Other:		

Action to be Taken:

Contact Purpose	☐ Glow	☐ Grow

Do more of what makes you happy.

Contact Documentation Form

Student Name: _____   Class: _____

Date and Time: _____   Person Initiating: _____

Person Contacted	□ Parent/Guardian:
	□ Counselor:
	□ Nurse:
	□ Administrator:
	□ Other:

Type of Contact	□ Phone Call/Text	□ Email
	□ Informal Meeting	□ Letter/Note
	□ Arranged Meeting	□ Class Dojo
	□ Other: _____	

Phone Call Response	□ No Answer	□ Wrong Number _____	□ Left Voicemail	□ Sent Text

Topic Discussed	□ Grades	□ Behavior
	□ Homework	□ Class work
	□ Projects	□ Schedule Meeting
Notes/Other:		

Action to be Taken:

Contact Purpose	□ Glow	□ Grow

Every master was once a beginner.

Contact Documentation Form

Student Name: _____   Class: _____

Date and Time: _____   Person Initiating: _____

Person Contacted	☐ Parent/Guardian:
	☐ Counselor:
	☐ Nurse:
	☐ Administrator:
	☐ Other:

Type of Contact	☐ Phone Call/Text	☐ Email
	☐ Informal Meeting	☐ Letter/Note
	☐ Arranged Meeting	☐ Class Dojo
	☐ Other: _____	

Phone Call Response	☐ No Answer	☐ Wrong Number _____	☐ Left Voicemail	☐ Sent Text

Topic Discussed	☐ Grades	☐ Behavior
	☐ Homework	☐ Class work
	☐ Projects	☐ Schedule Meeting
Notes/Other:		

Action to be Taken:

Contact Purpose	☐ Glow	☐ Grow

Don't hold on to thoughts that don't allow your mind to move forward.

Contact Documentation Form

Student Name: _____   Class: _____

Date and Time: _____   Person Initiating: _____

Person Contacted	☐ Parent/Guardian:
	☐ Counselor:
	☐ Nurse:
	☐ Administrator:
	☐ Other:

Type of Contact	☐ Phone Call/Text	☐ Email
	☐ Informal Meeting	☐ Letter/Note
	☐ Arranged Meeting	☐ Class Dojo
	☐ Other: _____	

Phone Call Response	☐ No Answer	☐ Wrong Number _____	☐ Left Voicemail	☐ Sent Text

Topic Discussed	☐ Grades	☐ Behavior
	☐ Homework	☐ Class work
	☐ Projects	☐ Schedule Meeting

Notes/Other:

Action to be Taken:

Contact Purpose	☐ Glow	☐ Grow

NOTE TO SELF: STOP TRYING SO HARD FOR PEOPLE WHO DON'T CARE.

Contact Documentation Form

Student Name: _____   Class: _____

Date and Time: _____   Person Initiating: _____

Person Contacted	☐ Parent/Guardian:
	☐ Counselor:
	☐ Nurse:
	☐ Administrator:
	☐ Other:

Type of Contact	☐ Phone Call/Text	☐ Email
	☐ Informal Meeting	☐ Letter/Note
	☐ Arranged Meeting	☐ Class Dojo
	☐ Other: _____	

Phone Call Response	☐ No Answer	☐ Wrong Number _____	☐ Left Voicemail	☐ Sent Text

Topic Discussed	☐ Grades	☐ Behavior
	☐ Homework	☐ Class work
	☐ Projects	☐ Schedule Meeting
Notes/Other:		

Action to be Taken:

Contact Purpose	☐ Glow	☐ Grow

Many a false step is made by standing still.

Contact Documentation Form

Student Name: _____   Class: _____

Date and Time: _____   Person Initiating: _____

Person Contacted	□ Parent/Guardian:
	□ Counselor:
	□ Nurse:
	□ Administrator:
	□ Other:

Type of Contact	□ Phone Call/Text	□ Email
	□ Informal Meeting	□ Letter/Note
	□ Arranged Meeting	□ Class Dojo
	□ Other: _____	

Phone Call Response	□ No Answer	□ Wrong Number _____	□ Left Voicemail	□ Sent Text

Topic Discussed	□ Grades	□ Behavior
	□ Homework	□ Class work
	□ Projects	□ Schedule Meeting
Notes/Other:		

Action to be Taken:

Contact Purpose	□ Glow	□ Grow

Know God, Know Peace.

Contact Documentation Form

Student Name: _____   Class: _____

Date and Time: _____   Person Initiating: _____

Person Contacted	☐ Parent/Guardian:	
	☐ Counselor:	
	☐ Nurse:	
	☐ Administrator:	
	☐ Other:	

Type of Contact	☐ Phone Call/Text	☐ Email
	☐ Informal Meeting	☐ Letter/Note
	☐ Arranged Meeting	☐ Class Dojo
	☐ Other: _____	

Phone Call Response	☐ No Answer	☐ Wrong Number _____	☐ Left Voicemail	☐ Sent Text

Topic Discussed	☐ Grades	☐ Behavior
	☐ Homework	☐ Class work
	☐ Projects	☐ Schedule Meeting
Notes/Other:		

Action to be Taken:

Contact Purpose	☐ Glow	☐ Grow

Accept everything you are and nothing you are not.

Contact Documentation Form

Student Name: _____   Class: _____

Date and Time: _____   Person Initiating: _____

Person Contacted	☐ Parent/Guardian:
	☐ Counselor:
	☐ Nurse:
	☐ Administrator:
	☐ Other:

Type of Contact	☐ Phone Call/Text	☐ Email
	☐ Informal Meeting	☐ Letter/Note
	☐ Arranged Meeting	☐ Class Dojo
	☐ Other: _____	

Phone Call Response	☐ No Answer	☐ Wrong Number _____	☐ Left Voicemail	☐ Sent Text

Topic Discussed	☐ Grades	☐ Behavior
	☐ Homework	☐ Class work
	☐ Projects	☐ Schedule Meeting
Notes/Other:		

Action to be Taken:

Contact Purpose	☐ Glow	☐ Grow

This will make perfect sense one day.

Contact Documentation Form

Student Name: _____   Class: _____

Date and Time: _____   Person Initiating: _____

Person Contacted	☐ Parent/Guardian:
	☐ Counselor:
	☐ Nurse:
	☐ Administrator:
	☐ Other:

Type of Contact	☐ Phone Call/Text	☐ Email
	☐ Informal Meeting	☐ Letter/Note
	☐ Arranged Meeting	☐ Class Dojo
	☐ Other: _____	

Phone Call Response	☐ No Answer	☐ Wrong Number _____	☐ Left Voicemail	☐ Sent Text

Topic Discussed	☐ Grades	☐ Behavior
	☐ Homework	☐ Class work
	☐ Projects	☐ Schedule Meeting
Notes/Other:		

Action to be Taken:

Contact Purpose	☐ Glow	☐ Grow

Remember to live.

Contact Documentation Form

Student Name: _____   Class: _____

Date and Time: _____   Person Initiating: _____

Person Contacted	□ Parent/Guardian:
	□ Counselor:
	□ Nurse:
	□ Administrator:
	□ Other:

Type of Contact	□ Phone Call/Text	□ Email
	□ Informal Meeting	□ Letter/Note
	□ Arranged Meeting	□ Class Dojo
	□ Other: _____	

Phone Call Response	□ No Answer	□ Wrong Number _____	□ Left Voicemail	□ Sent Text

Topic Discussed	□ Grades	□ Behavior
	□ Homework	□ Class work
	□ Projects	□ Schedule Meeting
Notes/Other:		

Action to be Taken:

Contact Purpose	□ Glow	□ Grow

It's okay if the only thing you did today was breathe.

Contact Documentation Form

Student Name: _____   Class: _____

Date and Time: _____   Person Initiating: _____

Person Contacted	☐ Parent/Guardian:
	☐ Counselor:
	☐ Nurse:
	☐ Administrator:
	☐ Other:

Type of Contact	☐ Phone Call/Text	☐ Email
	☐ Informal Meeting	☐ Letter/Note
	☐ Arranged Meeting	☐ Class Dojo
	☐ Other: _____	

Phone Call Response	☐ No Answer	☐ Wrong Number _____	☐ Left Voicemail	☐ Sent Text

Topic Discussed	☐ Grades	☐ Behavior
	☐ Homework	☐ Class work
	☐ Projects	☐ Schedule Meeting
Notes/Other:		

Action to be Taken:

Contact Purpose	☐ Glow	☐ Grow

Be selective in your battles. Sometimes peace is better than being right.

Contact Documentation Form

Student Name: _____   Class: _____

Date and Time: _____   Person Initiating: _____

Person Contacted	☐ Parent/Guardian:
	☐ Counselor:
	☐ Nurse:
	☐ Administrator:
	☐ Other:

Type of Contact	☐ Phone Call/Text	☐ Email
	☐ Informal Meeting	☐ Letter/Note
	☐ Arranged Meeting	☐ Class Dojo
	☐ Other: _____	

Phone Call Response	☐ No Answer	☐ Wrong Number _____	☐ Left Voicemail	☐ Sent Text

Topic Discussed	☐ Grades	☐ Behavior
	☐ Homework	☐ Class work
	☐ Projects	☐ Schedule Meeting
Notes/Other:		

Action to be Taken:

Contact Purpose	☐ Glow	☐ Grow

Why follow when you can LEAD.

Contact Documentation Form

Student Name: _____   Class: _____

Date and Time: _____   Person Initiating: _____

Person Contacted	☐ Parent/Guardian:
	☐ Counselor:
	☐ Nurse:
	☐ Administrator:
	☐ Other:

Type of Contact	☐ Phone Call/Text	☐ Email
	☐ Informal Meeting	☐ Letter/Note
	☐ Arranged Meeting	☐ Class Dojo
	☐ Other: _____	

Phone Call Response	☐ No Answer	☐ Wrong Number _____	☐ Left Voicemail	☐ Sent Text

Topic Discussed	☐ Grades	☐ Behavior
	☐ Homework	☐ Class work
	☐ Projects	☐ Schedule Meeting
Notes/Other:		

Action to be Taken:

Contact Purpose	☐ Glow	☐ Grow

Carpe Diem.

Contact Documentation Form

Student Name: _____   Class: _____

Date and Time: _____   Person Initiating: _____

Person Contacted	☐ Parent/Guardian:
	☐ Counselor:
	☐ Nurse:
	☐ Administrator:
	☐ Other:

Type of Contact	☐ Phone Call/Text	☐ Email
	☐ Informal Meeting	☐ Letter/Note
	☐ Arranged Meeting	☐ Class Dojo
	☐ Other: _____	

Phone Call Response	☐ No Answer	☐ Wrong Number _____	☐ Left Voicemail	☐ Sent Text

Topic Discussed	☐ Grades	☐ Behavior
	☐ Homework	☐ Class work
	☐ Projects	☐ Schedule Meeting

Notes/Other:

Action to be Taken:

Contact Purpose	☐ Glow	☐ Grow

Still I rise.

Contact Documentation Form

Student Name: _____   Class: _____

Date and Time: _____   Person Initiating: _____

Person Contacted	☐ Parent/Guardian:
	☐ Counselor:
	☐ Nurse:
	☐ Administrator:
	☐ Other:

Type of Contact	☐ Phone Call/Text	☐ Email
	☐ Informal Meeting	☐ Letter/Note
	☐ Arranged Meeting	☐ Class Dojo
	☐ Other: _____	

Phone Call Response	☐ No Answer	☐ Wrong Number _____	☐ Left Voicemail	☐ Sent Text

Topic Discussed	☐ Grades	☐ Behavior
	☐ Homework	☐ Class work
	☐ Projects	☐ Schedule Meeting
Notes/Other:		

Action to be Taken:

Contact Purpose	☐ Glow	☐ Grow

Coffee and kindness…maybe two coffees and then kindness.

Contact Documentation Form

Student Name: _____   Class: _____

Date and Time: _____   Person Initiating: _____

Person Contacted	□ Parent/Guardian:
	□ Counselor:
	□ Nurse:
	□ Administrator:
	□ Other:

Type of Contact	□ Phone Call/Text	□ Email
	□ Informal Meeting	□ Letter/Note
	□ Arranged Meeting	□ Class Dojo
	□ Other: _____	

Phone Call Response	□ No Answer	□ Wrong Number _____	□ Left Voicemail	□ Sent Text

Topic Discussed	□ Grades	□ Behavior
	□ Homework	□ Class work
	□ Projects	□ Schedule Meeting
Notes/Other:		

Action to be Taken:

Contact Purpose	□ Glow	□ Grow

THE DREAM IS FREE. THE HUSTLE IS SOLD SEPARATELY.

Contact Documentation Form

Student Name: _____   Class: _____

Date and Time: _____   Person Initiating: _____

Person Contacted	☐ Parent/Guardian:
	☐ Counselor:
	☐ Nurse:
	☐ Administrator:
	☐ Other:

Type of Contact	☐ Phone Call/Text	☐ Email
	☐ Informal Meeting	☐ Letter/Note
	☐ Arranged Meeting	☐ Class Dojo
	☐ Other: _____	

Phone Call Response	☐ No Answer	☐ Wrong Number _____	☐ Left Voicemail	☐ Sent Text

Topic Discussed	☐ Grades	☐ Behavior
	☐ Homework	☐ Class work
	☐ Projects	☐ Schedule Meeting
Notes/Other:		

Action to be Taken:

Contact Purpose	☐ Glow	☐ Grow

Stay strong. Your story isn't over yet.

Contact Documentation Form

Student Name: _____   Class: _____

Date and Time: _____   Person Initiating: _____

Person Contacted	☐ Parent/Guardian:
	☐ Counselor:
	☐ Nurse:
	☐ Administrator:
	☐ Other:

Type of Contact	☐ Phone Call/Text	☐ Email
	☐ Informal Meeting	☐ Letter/Note
	☐ Arranged Meeting	☐ Class Dojo
	☐ Other: _____	

Phone Call Response	☐ No Answer	☐ Wrong Number _____	☐ Left Voicemail	☐ Sent Text

Topic Discussed	☐ Grades	☐ Behavior
	☐ Homework	☐ Class work
	☐ Projects	☐ Schedule Meeting
Notes/Other:		

Action to be Taken:

Contact Purpose	☐ Glow	☐ Grow

Smile and walk away.

Contact Documentation Form

Student Name: _____   Class: _____

Date and Time: _____   Person Initiating: _____

Person Contacted	☐ Parent/Guardian:	
	☐ Counselor:	
	☐ Nurse:	
	☐ Administrator:	
	☐ Other:	

Type of Contact	☐ Phone Call/Text	☐ Email
	☐ Informal Meeting	☐ Letter/Note
	☐ Arranged Meeting	☐ Class Dojo
	☐ Other: _____	

Phone Call Response	☐ No Answer	☐ Wrong Number _____	☐ Left Voicemail	☐ Sent Text

Topic Discussed	☐ Grades	☐ Behavior
	☐ Homework	☐ Class work
	☐ Projects	☐ Schedule Meeting
Notes/Other:		

Action to be Taken:

Contact Purpose	☐ Glow	☐ Grow

Let gratitude be your attitude.

Contact Documentation Form

Student Name: _____   Class: _____

Date and Time: _____   Person Initiating: _____

Person Contacted	☐ Parent/Guardian:
	☐ Counselor:
	☐ Nurse:
	☐ Administrator:
	☐ Other:

Type of Contact	☐ Phone Call/Text	☐ Email
	☐ Informal Meeting	☐ Letter/Note
	☐ Arranged Meeting	☐ Class Dojo
	☐ Other: _____	

Phone Call Response	☐ No Answer	☐ Wrong Number _____	☐ Left Voicemail	☐ Sent Text

Topic Discussed	☐ Grades	☐ Behavior
	☐ Homework	☐ Class work
	☐ Projects	☐ Schedule Meeting
Notes/Other:		

Action to be Taken:

Contact Purpose	☐ Glow	☐ Grow

If you want the rainbow, you have to deal with the rain.

Contact Documentation Form

Student Name: _____   Class: _____

Date and Time: _____   Person Initiating: _____

Person Contacted	☐ Parent/Guardian:
	☐ Counselor:
	☐ Nurse:
	☐ Administrator:
	☐ Other:

Type of Contact	☐ Phone Call/Text	☐ Email
	☐ Informal Meeting	☐ Letter/Note
	☐ Arranged Meeting	☐ Class Dojo
	☐ Other: _____	

Phone Call Response	☐ No Answer	☐ Wrong Number _____	☐ Left Voicemail	☐ Sent Text

Topic Discussed	☐ Grades	☐ Behavior
	☐ Homework	☐ Class work
	☐ Projects	☐ Schedule Meeting
Notes/Other:		

Action to be Taken:

Contact Purpose	☐ Glow	☐ Grow

But God!

School Year

Whole Class Contact Documentation Form

Student Name	Contact Type	Response	Complete
1.	□ Call □ Text □ Email □Other	□ No Answer □ Left Voicemail □ Wrong #	□
2.	□ Call □ Text □ Email □Other	□ No Answer □ Left Voicemail □ Wrong #	□
3.	□ Call □ Text □ Email □Other	□ No Answer □ Left Voicemail □ Wrong #	□
4.	□ Call □ Text □ Email □Other	□ No Answer □ Left Voicemail □ Wrong #	□
5.	□ Call □ Text □ Email □Other	□ No Answer □ Left Voicemail □ Wrong #	□
6.	□ Call □ Text □ Email □Other	□ No Answer □ Left Voicemail □ Wrong #	□
7.	□ Call □ Text □ Email □Other	□ No Answer □ Left Voicemail □ Wrong #	□
8.	□ Call □ Text □ Email □Other	□ No Answer □ Left Voicemail □ Wrong #	□
9.	□ Call □ Text □ Email □Other	□ No Answer □ Left Voicemail □ Wrong #	□
10.	□ Call □ Text □ Email □Other	□ No Answer □ Left Voicemail □ Wrong #	□
11.	□ Call □ Text □ Email □Other	□ No Answer □ Left Voicemail □ Wrong #	□
12.	□ Call □ Text □ Email □Other	□ No Answer □ Left Voicemail □ Wrong #	□
13.	□ Call □ Text □ Email □Other	□ No Answer □ Left Voicemail □ Wrong #	□
14.	□ Call □ Text □ Email □Other	□ No Answer □ Left Voicemail □ Wrong #	□
15.	□ Call □ Text □ Email □Other	□ No Answer □ Left Voicemail □ Wrong #	□
16.	□ Call □ Text □ Email □Other	□ No Answer □ Left Voicemail □ Wrong #	□
17.	□ Call □ Text □ Email □Other	□ No Answer □ Left Voicemail □ Wrong #	□
18.	□ Call □ Text □ Email □Other	□ No Answer □ Left Voicemail □ Wrong #	□
19.	□ Call □ Text □ Email □Other	□ No Answer □ Left Voicemail □ Wrong #	□
20.	□ Call □ Text □ Email □Other	□ No Answer □ Left Voicemail □ Wrong #	□
21.	□ Call □ Text □ Email □Other	□ No Answer □ Left Voicemail □ Wrong #	□
22.	□ Call □ Text □ Email □Other	□ No Answer □ Left Voicemail □ Wrong #	□

Student Name	Contact Type	Response	Complete
	□ Call □ Text □ Email □ Other	□ No Answer □ Left Voicemail □ Wrong #	□
	□ Call □ Text □ Email □ Other	□ No Answer □ Left Voicemail □ Wrong #	□
	□ Call □ Text □ Email □ Other	□ No Answer □ Left Voicemail □ Wrong #	□
	□ Call □ Text □ Email □ Other	□ No Answer □ Left Voicemail □ Wrong #	□
	□ Call □ Text □ Email □ Other	□ No Answer □ Left Voicemail □ Wrong #	□
	□ Call □ Text □ Email □ Other	□ No Answer □ Left Voicemail □ Wrong #	□
	□ Call □ Text □ Email □ Other	□ No Answer □ Left Voicemail □ Wrong #	□
	□ Call □ Text □ Email □ Other	□ No Answer □ Left Voicemail □ Wrong #	□
	□ Call □ Text □ Email □ Other	□ No Answer □ Left Voicemail □ Wrong #	□
	□ Call □ Text □ Email □ Other	□ No Answer □ Left Voicemail □ Wrong #	□
	□ Call □ Text □ Email □ Other	□ No Answer □ Left Voicemail □ Wrong #	□
	□ Call □ Text □ Email □ Other	□ No Answer □ Left Voicemail □ Wrong #	□
	□ Call □ Text □ Email □ Other	□ No Answer □ Left Voicemail □ Wrong #	□
	□ Call □ Text □ Email □ Other	□ No Answer □ Left Voicemail □ Wrong #	□
	□ Call □ Text □ Email □ Other	□ No Answer □ Left Voicemail □ Wrong #	□
	□ Call □ Text □ Email □ Other	□ No Answer □ Left Voicemail □ Wrong #	□
	□ Call □ Text □ Email □ Other	□ No Answer □ Left Voicemail □ Wrong #	□
	□ Call □ Text □ Email □ Other	□ No Answer □ Left Voicemail □ Wrong #	□
	□ Call □ Text □ Email □ Other	□ No Answer □ Left Voicemail □ Wrong #	□
	□ Call □ Text □ Email □ Other	□ No Answer □ Left Voicemail □ Wrong #	□
	□ Call □ Text □ Email □ Other	□ No Answer □ Left Voicemail □ Wrong #	□
	□ Call □ Text □ Email □ Other	□ No Answer □ Left Voicemail □ Wrong #	□
	□ Call □ Text □ Email □ Other	□ No Answer □ Left Voicemail □ Wrong #	□

Whole Class Contact Documentation Form

Student Name	Contact Type	Response	Complete
1.	□ Call □ Text □ Email □ Other	□ No Answer □ Left Voicemail □ Wrong #	□
2.	□ Call □ Text □ Email □ Other	□ No Answer □ Left Voicemail □ Wrong #	□
3.	□ Call □ Text □ Email □ Other	□ No Answer □ Left Voicemail □ Wrong #	□
4.	□ Call □ Text □ Email □ Other	□ No Answer □ Left Voicemail □ Wrong #	□
5.	□ Call □ Text □ Email □ Other	□ No Answer □ Left Voicemail □ Wrong #	□
6.	□ Call □ Text □ Email □ Other	□ No Answer □ Left Voicemail □ Wrong #	□
7.	□ Call □ Text □ Email □ Other	□ No Answer □ Left Voicemail □ Wrong #	□
8.	□ Call □ Text □ Email □ Other	□ No Answer □ Left Voicemail □ Wrong #	□
9.	□ Call □ Text □ Email □ Other	□ No Answer □ Left Voicemail □ Wrong #	□
10.	□ Call □ Text □ Email □ Other	□ No Answer □ Left Voicemail □ Wrong #	□
11.	□ Call □ Text □ Email □ Other	□ No Answer □ Left Voicemail □ Wrong #	□
12.	□ Call □ Text □ Email □ Other	□ No Answer □ Left Voicemail □ Wrong #	□
13.	□ Call □ Text □ Email □ Other	□ No Answer □ Left Voicemail □ Wrong #	□
14.	□ Call □ Text □ Email □ Other	□ No Answer □ Left Voicemail □ Wrong #	□
15.	□ Call □ Text □ Email □ Other	□ No Answer □ Left Voicemail □ Wrong #	□
16.	□ Call □ Text □ Email □ Other	□ No Answer □ Left Voicemail □ Wrong #	□
17.	□ Call □ Text □ Email □ Other	□ No Answer □ Left Voicemail □ Wrong #	□
18.	□ Call □ Text □ Email □ Other	□ No Answer □ Left Voicemail □ Wrong #	□
19.	□ Call □ Text □ Email □ Other	□ No Answer □ Left Voicemail □ Wrong #	□
20.	□ Call □ Text □ Email □ Other	□ No Answer □ Left Voicemail □ Wrong #	□
21.	□ Call □ Text □ Email □ Other	□ No Answer □ Left Voicemail □ Wrong #	□
22.	□ Call □ Text □ Email □ Other	□ No Answer □ Left Voicemail □ Wrong #	□

Student Name	Contact Type	Response	Complete
	□ Call □ Text □ Email □ Other	□ No Answer □ Left Voicemail □ Wrong #	□
	□ Call □ Text □ Email □ Other	□ No Answer □ Left Voicemail □ Wrong #	□
	□ Call □ Text □ Email □ Other	□ No Answer □ Left Voicemail □ Wrong #	□
	□ Call □ Text □ Email □ Other	□ No Answer □ Left Voicemail □ Wrong #	□
	□ Call □ Text □ Email □ Other	□ No Answer □ Left Voicemail □ Wrong #	□
	□ Call □ Text □ Email □ Other	□ No Answer □ Left Voicemail □ Wrong #	□
	□ Call □ Text □ Email □ Other	□ No Answer □ Left Voicemail □ Wrong #	□
	□ Call □ Text □ Email □ Other	□ No Answer □ Left Voicemail □ Wrong #	□
	□ Call □ Text □ Email □ Other	□ No Answer □ Left Voicemail □ Wrong #	□
	□ Call □ Text □ Email □ Other	□ No Answer □ Left Voicemail □ Wrong #	□
	□ Call □ Text □ Email □ Other	□ No Answer □ Left Voicemail □ Wrong #	□
	□ Call □ Text □ Email □ Other	□ No Answer □ Left Voicemail □ Wrong #	□
	□ Call □ Text □ Email □ Other	□ No Answer □ Left Voicemail □ Wrong #	□
	□ Call □ Text □ Email □ Other	□ No Answer □ Left Voicemail □ Wrong #	□
	□ Call □ Text □ Email □ Other	□ No Answer □ Left Voicemail □ Wrong #	□
	□ Call □ Text □ Email □ Other	□ No Answer □ Left Voicemail □ Wrong #	□
	□ Call □ Text □ Email □ Other	□ No Answer □ Left Voicemail □ Wrong #	□
	□ Call □ Text □ Email □ Other	□ No Answer □ Left Voicemail □ Wrong #	□
	□ Call □ Text □ Email □ Other	□ No Answer □ Left Voicemail □ Wrong #	□
	□ Call □ Text □ Email □ Other	□ No Answer □ Left Voicemail □ Wrong #	□
	□ Call □ Text □ Email □ Other	□ No Answer □ Left Voicemail □ Wrong #	□
	□ Call □ Text □ Email □ Other	□ No Answer □ Left Voicemail □ Wrong #	□
	□ Call □ Text □ Email □ Other	□ No Answer □ Left Voicemail □ Wrong #	□

Whole Class Contact Documentation Form

Student Name	Contact Type	Response	Complete
1.	□ Call □ Text □ Email □ Other	□ No Answer □ Left Voicemail □ Wrong #	□
2.	□ Call □ Text □ Email □ Other	□ No Answer □ Left Voicemail □ Wrong #	□
3.	□ Call □ Text □ Email □ Other	□ No Answer □ Left Voicemail □ Wrong #	□
4.	□ Call □ Text □ Email □ Other	□ No Answer □ Left Voicemail □ Wrong #	□
5.	□ Call □ Text □ Email □ Other	□ No Answer □ Left Voicemail □ Wrong #	□
6.	□ Call □ Text □ Email □ Other	□ No Answer □ Left Voicemail □ Wrong #	□
7.	□ Call □ Text □ Email □ Other	□ No Answer □ Left Voicemail □ Wrong #	□
8.	□ Call □ Text □ Email □ Other	□ No Answer □ Left Voicemail □ Wrong #	□
9.	□ Call □ Text □ Email □ Other	□ No Answer □ Left Voicemail □ Wrong #	□
10.	□ Call □ Text □ Email □ Other	□ No Answer □ Left Voicemail □ Wrong #	□
11.	□ Call □ Text □ Email □ Other	□ No Answer □ Left Voicemail □ Wrong #	□
12.	□ Call □ Text □ Email □ Other	□ No Answer □ Left Voicemail □ Wrong #	□
13.	□ Call □ Text □ Email □ Other	□ No Answer □ Left Voicemail □ Wrong #	□
14.	□ Call □ Text □ Email □ Other	□ No Answer □ Left Voicemail □ Wrong #	□
15.	□ Call □ Text □ Email □ Other	□ No Answer □ Left Voicemail □ Wrong #	□
16.	□ Call □ Text □ Email □ Other	□ No Answer □ Left Voicemail □ Wrong #	□
17.	□ Call □ Text □ Email □ Other	□ No Answer □ Left Voicemail □ Wrong #	□
18.	□ Call □ Text □ Email □ Other	□ No Answer □ Left Voicemail □ Wrong #	□
19.	□ Call □ Text □ Email □ Other	□ No Answer □ Left Voicemail □ Wrong #	□
20.	□ Call □ Text □ Email □ Other	□ No Answer □ Left Voicemail □ Wrong #	□
21.	□ Call □ Text □ Email □ Other	□ No Answer □ Left Voicemail □ Wrong #	□
22.	□ Call □ Text □ Email □ Other	□ No Answer □ Left Voicemail □ Wrong #	□

Student Name	Contact Type	Response	Complete
	□ Call □ Text □ Email □ Other	□ No Answer □ Left Voicemail □ Wrong #	□
	□ Call □ Text □ Email □ Other	□ No Answer □ Left Voicemail □ Wrong #	□
	□ Call □ Text □ Email □ Other	□ No Answer □ Left Voicemail □ Wrong #	□
	□ Call □ Text □ Email □ Other	□ No Answer □ Left Voicemail □ Wrong #	□
	□ Call □ Text □ Email □ Other	□ No Answer □ Left Voicemail □ Wrong #	□
	□ Call □ Text □ Email □ Other	□ No Answer □ Left Voicemail □ Wrong #	□
	□ Call □ Text □ Email □ Other	□ No Answer □ Left Voicemail □ Wrong #	□
	□ Call □ Text □ Email □ Other	□ No Answer □ Left Voicemail □ Wrong #	□
	□ Call □ Text □ Email □ Other	□ No Answer □ Left Voicemail □ Wrong #	□
	□ Call □ Text □ Email □ Other	□ No Answer □ Left Voicemail □ Wrong #	□
	□ Call □ Text □ Email □ Other	□ No Answer □ Left Voicemail □ Wrong #	□
	□ Call □ Text □ Email □ Other	□ No Answer □ Left Voicemail □ Wrong #	□
	□ Call □ Text □ Email □ Other	□ No Answer □ Left Voicemail □ Wrong #	□
	□ Call □ Text □ Email □ Other	□ No Answer □ Left Voicemail □ Wrong #	□
	□ Call □ Text □ Email □ Other	□ No Answer □ Left Voicemail □ Wrong #	□
	□ Call □ Text □ Email □ Other	□ No Answer □ Left Voicemail □ Wrong #	□
	□ Call □ Text □ Email □ Other	□ No Answer □ Left Voicemail □ Wrong #	□
	□ Call □ Text □ Email □ Other	□ No Answer □ Left Voicemail □ Wrong #	□
	□ Call □ Text □ Email □ Other	□ No Answer □ Left Voicemail □ Wrong #	□
	□ Call □ Text □ Email □ Other	□ No Answer □ Left Voicemail □ Wrong #	□
	□ Call □ Text □ Email □ Other	□ No Answer □ Left Voicemail □ Wrong #	□
	□ Call □ Text □ Email □ Other	□ No Answer □ Left Voicemail □ Wrong #	□

214

Whole Class Contact Documentation Form

Student Name	Contact Type	Response	Complete
1.	□ Call □ Text □ Email □ Other	□ No Answer □ Left Voicemail □ Wrong #	□
2.	□ Call □ Text □ Email □ Other	□ No Answer □ Left Voicemail □ Wrong #	□
3.	□ Call □ Text □ Email □ Other	□ No Answer □ Left Voicemail □ Wrong #	□
4.	□ Call □ Text □ Email □ Other	□ No Answer □ Left Voicemail □ Wrong #	□
5.	□ Call □ Text □ Email □ Other	□ No Answer □ Left Voicemail □ Wrong #	□
6.	□ Call □ Text □ Email □ Other	□ No Answer □ Left Voicemail □ Wrong #	□
7.	□ Call □ Text □ Email □ Other	□ No Answer □ Left Voicemail □ Wrong #	□
8.	□ Call □ Text □ Email □ Other	□ No Answer □ Left Voicemail □ Wrong #	□
9.	□ Call □ Text □ Email □ Other	□ No Answer □ Left Voicemail □ Wrong #	□
10.	□ Call □ Text □ Email □ Other	□ No Answer □ Left Voicemail □ Wrong #	□
11.	□ Call □ Text □ Email □ Other	□ No Answer □ Left Voicemail □ Wrong #	□
12.	□ Call □ Text □ Email □ Other	□ No Answer □ Left Voicemail □ Wrong #	□
13.	□ Call □ Text □ Email □ Other	□ No Answer □ Left Voicemail □ Wrong #	□
14.	□ Call □ Text □ Email □ Other	□ No Answer □ Left Voicemail □ Wrong #	□
15.	□ Call □ Text □ Email □ Other	□ No Answer □ Left Voicemail □ Wrong #	□
16.	□ Call □ Text □ Email □ Other	□ No Answer □ Left Voicemail □ Wrong #	□
17.	□ Call □ Text □ Email □ Other	□ No Answer □ Left Voicemail □ Wrong #	□
18.	□ Call □ Text □ Email □ Other	□ No Answer □ Left Voicemail □ Wrong #	□
19.	□ Call □ Text □ Email □ Other	□ No Answer □ Left Voicemail □ Wrong #	□
20.	□ Call □ Text □ Email □ Other	□ No Answer □ Left Voicemail □ Wrong #	□
21.	□ Call □ Text □ Email □ Other	□ No Answer □ Left Voicemail □ Wrong #	□
22.	□ Call □ Text □ Email □ Other	□ No Answer □ Left Voicemail □ Wrong #	□

Student Name	Contact Type	Response	Complete
	□ Call □ Text □ Email □ Other	□ No Answer □ Left Voicemail □ Wrong #	□
	□ Call □ Text □ Email □ Other	□ No Answer □ Left Voicemail □ Wrong #	□
	□ Call □ Text □ Email □ Other	□ No Answer □ Left Voicemail □ Wrong #	□
	□ Call □ Text □ Email □ Other	□ No Answer □ Left Voicemail □ Wrong #	□
	□ Call □ Text □ Email □ Other	□ No Answer □ Left Voicemail □ Wrong #	□
	□ Call □ Text □ Email □ Other	□ No Answer □ Left Voicemail □ Wrong #	□
	□ Call □ Text □ Email □ Other	□ No Answer □ Left Voicemail □ Wrong #	□
	□ Call □ Text □ Email □ Other	□ No Answer □ Left Voicemail □ Wrong #	□
	□ Call □ Text □ Email □ Other	□ No Answer □ Left Voicemail □ Wrong #	□
	□ Call □ Text □ Email □ Other	□ No Answer □ Left Voicemail □ Wrong #	□
	□ Call □ Text □ Email □ Other	□ No Answer □ Left Voicemail □ Wrong #	□
	□ Call □ Text □ Email □ Other	□ No Answer □ Left Voicemail □ Wrong #	□
	□ Call □ Text □ Email □ Other	□ No Answer □ Left Voicemail □ Wrong #	□
	□ Call □ Text □ Email □ Other	□ No Answer □ Left Voicemail □ Wrong #	□
	□ Call □ Text □ Email □ Other	□ No Answer □ Left Voicemail □ Wrong #	□
	□ Call □ Text □ Email □ Other	□ No Answer □ Left Voicemail □ Wrong #	□
	□ Call □ Text □ Email □ Other	□ No Answer □ Left Voicemail □ Wrong #	□
	□ Call □ Text □ Email □ Other	□ No Answer □ Left Voicemail □ Wrong #	□
	□ Call □ Text □ Email □ Other	□ No Answer □ Left Voicemail □ Wrong #	□
	□ Call □ Text □ Email □ Other	□ No Answer □ Left Voicemail □ Wrong #	□
	□ Call □ Text □ Email □ Other	□ No Answer □ Left Voicemail □ Wrong #	□
	□ Call □ Text □ Email □ Other	□ No Answer □ Left Voicemail □ Wrong #	□
	□ Call □ Text □ Email □ Other	□ No Answer □ Left Voicemail □ Wrong #	□

Whole Class Contact Documentation Form

Student Name	Contact Type	Response	Complete
1.	□ Call □ Text □ Email □ Other	□ No Answer □ Left Voicemail □ Wrong #	□
2.	□ Call □ Text □ Email □ Other	□ No Answer □ Left Voicemail □ Wrong #	□
3.	□ Call □ Text □ Email □ Other	□ No Answer □ Left Voicemail □ Wrong #	□
4.	□ Call □ Text □ Email □ Other	□ No Answer □ Left Voicemail □ Wrong #	□
5.	□ Call □ Text □ Email □ Other	□ No Answer □ Left Voicemail □ Wrong #	□
6.	□ Call □ Text □ Email □ Other	□ No Answer □ Left Voicemail □ Wrong #	□
7.	□ Call □ Text □ Email □ Other	□ No Answer □ Left Voicemail □ Wrong #	□
8.	□ Call □ Text □ Email □ Other	□ No Answer □ Left Voicemail □ Wrong #	□
9.	□ Call □ Text □ Email □ Other	□ No Answer □ Left Voicemail □ Wrong #	□
10.	□ Call □ Text □ Email □ Other	□ No Answer □ Left Voicemail □ Wrong #	□
11.	□ Call □ Text □ Email □ Other	□ No Answer □ Left Voicemail □ Wrong #	□
12.	□ Call □ Text □ Email □ Other	□ No Answer □ Left Voicemail □ Wrong #	□
13.	□ Call □ Text □ Email □ Other	□ No Answer □ Left Voicemail □ Wrong #	□
14.	□ Call □ Text □ Email □ Other	□ No Answer □ Left Voicemail □ Wrong #	□
15.	□ Call □ Text □ Email □ Other	□ No Answer □ Left Voicemail □ Wrong #	□
16.	□ Call □ Text □ Email □ Other	□ No Answer □ Left Voicemail □ Wrong #	□
17.	□ Call □ Text □ Email □ Other	□ No Answer □ Left Voicemail □ Wrong #	□
18.	□ Call □ Text □ Email □ Other	□ No Answer □ Left Voicemail □ Wrong #	□
19.	□ Call □ Text □ Email □ Other	□ No Answer □ Left Voicemail □ Wrong #	□
20.	□ Call □ Text □ Email □ Other	□ No Answer □ Left Voicemail □ Wrong #	□
21.	□ Call □ Text □ Email □ Other	□ No Answer □ Left Voicemail □ Wrong #	□
22.	□ Call □ Text □ Email □ Other	□ No Answer □ Left Voicemail □ Wrong #	□

Student Name	Contact Type	Response	Complete
	□ Call □ Text □ Email □ Other	□ No Answer □ Left Voicemail □ Wrong #	□
	□ Call □ Text □ Email □ Other	□ No Answer □ Left Voicemail □ Wrong #	□
	□ Call □ Text □ Email □ Other	□ No Answer □ Left Voicemail □ Wrong #	□
	□ Call □ Text □ Email □ Other	□ No Answer □ Left Voicemail □ Wrong #	□
	□ Call □ Text □ Email □ Other	□ No Answer □ Left Voicemail □ Wrong #	□
	□ Call □ Text □ Email □ Other	□ No Answer □ Left Voicemail □ Wrong #	□
	□ Call □ Text □ Email □ Other	□ No Answer □ Left Voicemail □ Wrong #	□
	□ Call □ Text □ Email □ Other	□ No Answer □ Left Voicemail □ Wrong #	□
	□ Call □ Text □ Email □ Other	□ No Answer □ Left Voicemail □ Wrong #	□
	□ Call □ Text □ Email □ Other	□ No Answer □ Left Voicemail □ Wrong #	□
	□ Call □ Text □ Email □ Other	□ No Answer □ Left Voicemail □ Wrong #	□
	□ Call □ Text □ Email □ Other	□ No Answer □ Left Voicemail □ Wrong #	□
	□ Call □ Text □ Email □ Other	□ No Answer □ Left Voicemail □ Wrong #	□
	□ Call □ Text □ Email □ Other	□ No Answer □ Left Voicemail □ Wrong #	□
	□ Call □ Text □ Email □ Other	□ No Answer □ Left Voicemail □ Wrong #	□
	□ Call □ Text □ Email □ Other	□ No Answer □ Left Voicemail □ Wrong #	□
	□ Call □ Text □ Email □ Other	□ No Answer □ Left Voicemail □ Wrong #	□
	□ Call □ Text □ Email □ Other	□ No Answer □ Left Voicemail □ Wrong #	□
	□ Call □ Text □ Email □ Other	□ No Answer □ Left Voicemail □ Wrong #	□
	□ Call □ Text □ Email □ Other	□ No Answer □ Left Voicemail □ Wrong #	□
	□ Call □ Text □ Email □ Other	□ No Answer □ Left Voicemail □ Wrong #	□
	□ Call □ Text □ Email □ Other	□ No Answer □ Left Voicemail □ Wrong #	□
	□ Call □ Text □ Email □ Other	□ No Answer □ Left Voicemail □ Wrong #	□

Made in the USA
Monee, IL
07 January 2021